HAPPINESS IS A WAR

Also by David Peterson

Yellowstone: Like No Other Place On Earth
An Exploration of the Tetons
Portrait of Yellowstone
Yellowstone: Near, Far and Wild

**David
Peterson**

June 22 2024

Enjoy the book Cheryl!

Happiness is a Warm Carcass™

Assorted Sordid Stories from the Photographer in the Midst

Published by David Peterson
www.photographerinthemidst.com

The chapter entitled "The Sorcerer's Yellow Stone" first appeared in *Outside Bozeman* in slightly different form.

The chapter entitled "Bluffing (or Big Rock Candy Chickenheads)" and previously titled "Dillingham Blues" is dedicated to the memory of good friend and fellow "Hamster" Ron Dilling.

A special thanks to Mike England—the bravest publisher out there.
Thanks also to the people at Farcountry Press for their patience over the years.

Design and cover photo by the author.
Author photo by "Tex."

ISBN: 978-1-59152-155-6

s**ʊ**eetgrassbooks

Produced by Sweetgrass Books,
PO Box 5630, Helena MT 58604
(800) 821- 3874
www.sweetgrassbooks.com

Produced and printed in the United States of America.

To consumers of free range Happy Meals everywhere.

CONTENTS

CONTENTS (continued)

Introduction

The world of literature is filled with people going undercover. Just off the top of my head I seem to recall an author posing as a hotel chambermaid before writing an "exposé" based on her experiences. Someone else had the idea, I think, to write a "tell-all" book about becoming a professional dishwasher in all fifty states.

I guess it passed for human interest.

The most famous case (and one that's actually interesting), however, is that of journalist George Plimpton, who wrote his best selling book *Paper Lion* after masquerading as a free agent college quarterback trying out for the Detroit Lions football team.

So why not infiltrate the world of professional nature photography? Why not go behind the "scenics" and write about photography's more seamy side? I'll tell you why. Because it's as ridiculous and unnecessary as the first two examples I cited. There's no seamy side to nature photography. And who would ever think there was?

But I did it anyway.

And a funny thing happened. Unlike George Plimpton, I actually made the team! Okay, it was as fourth-string punter on an Arena League franchise. But there I was, making money as a photographer, and having to postpone this book by about twenty-five years.

Before I made the team, though, I probably washed a hundred times as many dishes, and cleaned maybe ten more rooms than the aforementioned snooty authors. (Seems you don't just "become" even a mediocre professional photographer without paying at least some dues).

But I did eventually quit my day jobs and for whatever reason—along with selling photos—began preparing this very manuscript.

As such, the following stories (in no particular order) span the time frame from the early eighties to the present, where I'm sitting on a beach chair in Thailand writing this introduction—and hoping that the swelling in my right foot isn't a rare (or even common) form of elephantiasis.

Based loosely on imaginary events (kind of strange, I have to admit—for an exposé), these accounts go behind the scenes of a quasi-nomad (me) who is loosely based in Yellowstone National Park. I say *loosely*, because I've also found myself living (during the Yellowstone off-season, of course) everywhere from Fargo North Dakota, to the Geylang district of Singapore City, Singapore. Temporary jobs—until full-time professional photographer status could be attained—have ranged from carwash "rear end wiper," to house-sitter, cook, and one short stint as a hotel chambermaid.

Yeah, I know—barely human interest.

What's more, this less-than-compelling content—when combined with nicknames, nicknames given to my many various vehicles, friends, girlfriends, pets, body parts and personalities ("Jumbo"—my right foot—for instance, is currently developing a split-personality all his own), and countless obscure references (see George Plimpton) will also *confuse* you—if it hasn't already.

David "Slash" Peterson (or Dave/Peterson) is all over the place, literally, figuratively and grammatically—often using unnecessary and extremely annoying word/punctuation-play whenever he sees fit, and sometimes even slips into the third-person point-of-view when writing about himself.

Keep in mind, though, that regardless of his/*my* many manifestations elsewhere, I always seem to return to Yellowstone.

During one of my stays in China, for example, my non-English-speaking taxi driver took me (presumably) to the spot I pointed out on a map. It was a nice place, and vaguely familiar. But it wasn't where I wanted to go. So the next day, after pointing out a different location on the map, to a different driver, I ended up at the same place. The next day, after pointing to a spot on the other *side* of the map, I again found myself at the same scenic overlook. So the next day, after pointing to "Chromosome x22" on a map of the human genome that I just happened to have bookmarked on my iPad (Google Street-View is amazing), I, of course, ended up at the same no-longer-only-vaguely-familiar area—riding past the very same landmarks that I'd memorized on the previous three rides. It was only later, of course, that I thought to read the English translation of the location. It translated to: Yellow Stone Stronghold.

You see? I always return to Yellowstone.

And a lifetime of pursuing a career in nature photography is filled with insecurity, instability, and misunderstanding—at least the way I did it. In that sense, these are *cautionary* loosely-based-on-imaginary-events tales. Insult and injury abound.

But the cold dry air of Northwest Wyoming (or just the thought of it sometimes) has a way of healing all that ails you—physically and mentally. It's never far from my mind or my lungs. That said, it kind of makes me wonder why "Jumbo" is beginning to grow tusks?

Dave Peterson

Please Don't Eat
the Butter & Egg Plants

When my friend Rob "*The* Tour Guide" Doran offered to give me a free bus tour I was apprehensive. And who could blame me? I recalled a similar offer made years ago by a manager-type at Yellowstone's Mammoth Hot Springs restaurant. She showed me where they stacked the tubs, walked me by the napkin folding station, guided me by the silverware receptacles at the dish station, and then into a back room where she gave me an unexpected and completely inappropriate little buss on the cheek.

"I hope this isn't going to end badly," I said to Rob.

"Don't worry," he replied before getting into character and starting the tour. "Now over here we have the right-side rear-view mirror . . ."

We then walked toward the back of the bus as he showed me the running lights, the storage compartments, and finally the rear bumper.

"You want a tour of the *inside* now?" Rob continued.

"I won't have to do anything unseemly—like go to *work*?" I asked.

"I mean, you're not going to make me your busboy are you?"

"Relax, it's just a joke," he said.

"I know that."

In fact, I knew that it was the oldest tour guide joke in the book, but that didn't keep me from being traumatized. And Rob felt so bad about it all that he told me that if there were any empty seats available I could ride along on the *real* tour of Yellowstone.

"And be traumatized by *more* of your jokes?"

"It's your call," he said, but I've got a charter tour today—chartered by a group of Swedish swimsuit models on vacation."

The only question at that point was how to say *yes* in Swedish. Oh, yeah—*ja*.

We started out in the northern end of Yellowstone where wolves, bears, and large ungulates were a fairly common sight. This day, however, was a fairly uncommon one—we saw nothing but small animals.

"Vatter dose chipmunks on der road called?" someone asked.

"Chipmunks," Rob replied with a straight face, before then yielding. "Actually, the scientific term is 'Suicidal Chipmunks.' We drivers hate them because we're always having to yield."

"Vat vas dat vun doing?"

"Eating his recently flattened buddy," Rob answered truthfully.

The models, their collective stomach-gurgling at times drowning out the bus, looked around at each other nervously and popped some diuretics into their mouths. And they'd apparently long-since run out of appetite suppressants, so we stopped to eat. Actually we stopped to pee, but some of the passengers noticed a patch of wild strawberries and went for it.

Back on the road we soon passed a little-known Yellowstone cultural site.

"This is the approximate location," Rob informed us, "where famed directors William Hanna and Joseph Barbera had 'Mr. Ranger Sir' place a telemetry collar and tie on a tranquilized Yogi in episode 43: 'Spy Guys.'"

"Vas dere a speaker in der tie clasp?" the lead Swede asked.

"Yeah. How'd you know that?" Rob asked back.

"I tink I saw dat vun on SVED-TV," came the reply. "Poor Jogi, he taut it vas his conscience speaking to him und almost gave up stealing—how do you say—*picnic baskets*."

"It's pronounced pic-i-*nic* basket."

A group-drool occurred as they all re-pronounced it correctly.

Pretty soon though, the latest dose of diuretics kicked in and we once again had to stop.

"Vatter dose pretty jellow flowers?" one of them asked between handfuls of huckleberries. "Jellow Yackets?"

"No, they're really just weeds," Rob said, waiting in line with everyone else, "non-native flowers called Yellow Toadflax. The more common name for them, though, is Butter & Egg Plant."

The tourists began to drool again as Rob quickly advised them that they probably shouldn't try eating them. "They might not be safe."

Back on the road and heading south we then drove past an area called Fishing Bridge.

"In the Fifties," Rob began, "you were allowed to fish from the bridge. And in those days it was a destination almost as famous as Old Faithful, almost as crowded too—which caused problems. You see, whenever a trout was hooked, which was often, roughly two dozen lines got crossed, leading to cross words and eventually several fish-fights."

"*That* was lame," I said to Rob after he hung up the microphone.

"Do you want to do this?" he shot back.

I quickly grabbed the mike. "And there's nothing quite like fresh-caught Yellowstone Cutthroat, to reduce the swelling of black eyes caused by fish-fights. Later you'd fry the fish up in cornmeal and . . ."

"It was a figure of speech," Rob said.

I then reminded Rob that he needed to shift gears, and demanded he take the bus to Havana.

"We're at a stop sign," he replied. "And how about Lake Village instead?"

7

"The Lake Hotel," I informed everyone as we later drove by it, "was built a long time ago—by some guy, uh . . ."

"Renovated . . . 1903 . . . Robert Reamer," Rob stage-whispered.

"And renovated in 1903 by Robert Reamer." I continued. "But there was a *restoration* project in the 1980s that . . ."

"Oh, that's right," Rob gleefully interrupted (a little too gleefully I thought). "Didn't you use to—*work*—there then?"

Rob really knew how to hurt a guy, but I carried on. "Yes," I said into the mike, "but back then I was what's known as a Linen Brother. We didn't usually have much to do, mostly going from linen closet to laundry and back saying the words *'rrrrrrruuuubber biscuit'* a lot."

And for a moment *both* Rob and I thought he had forgotten to shift, but ultimately came to recognize the subtle differences between sounds made by gears, and those made by the insurgent Swedish stomachs—fish & biscuits being one of their favorite guilty pleasures.

"Anyway, it was one of those slow afternoons," I continued, "when my brother-in-linen, a guy named Elwood, suggested we go explore the old hotel's attic. He had the master key to every door *and* seniority on me. So he also suggested that *I* go *first*. And, indeed, I'm guessing I would have been the first person in at least 20 *years* to have set foot in there. So I first peeked my head in to get adjusted to the darkness and noticed a thick substance, assumed to be insulation overspray, coating one of the pillars. It kinda' looked alive. But I also assumed that was just my eyes playing tricks on me—adjusting to the darkness and all. Then I tested thc 'insulation' directly under my outstretched right foot. 'One small step for a Linen Brother;' I said making the plunge, 'one giant . . . *foof.*'"

"Uff da! Vat vas vit dere '*foof?*'"

"Well it seems the stuff I *thought* was insulation—but wasn't—completely covered a flight of stairs hiding three small steps *downward*. And 'foof' was the sound Elwood said my face made upon impact with the guano."

"Vat vas vit dere guano?"

"What he means," Rob explained, regaining the microphone, "is that he accidentally walked in on an occupied *bat*room."

"There are no accidents," I reminded Rob.

"Sounds like dere vas *billions* of tiny little accidents," the lead Swede giggled, getting the rest to giggle too—and thus *jiggle*.

I looked the other way and Rob kept his eyes on the road.

"Vat happened den, after der foof?"

"In slightly over my head," I said, "I sorta' dog-paddled back to 'shore'—stage 13-b, I think, in Sigmund Freud's personality-development process. I later helped out the refurbishers—who were of course in charge of correcting the bat problem, by taking a few five-gallon pickle buckets of the guano back home to my parents garden."

"Pickles," the models all moaned together.

Rob, back in control now, tried to cleanse the conversational palette as we drove along.

"Now out to your right is where, it's said, occurred one of the most popular of all Yellowstone myths. Parents wishing to get a photo of a black bear licking their child's face, supposedly smeared honey on said face in order to entice the bear."

A group lip-smack ensued, as *I* bit my *tongue*. I wanted to tell them how I tried that trick myself with a co-worker name Molly, only with no camera, bear, child, or face involved, but didn't want to encourage the models, some of whom *were* wistfully eying my right cheek.

"It, of course, ended in disaster—or so they say," Rob concluded.

"Tell me about it," I added.

"Vere *ere* dere bears?" an impatient passenger then wanted to know.

"They're mostly all in the backcountry these days," Rob said. "We probably won't see one today."

"We probably won't see Bigfoot either," I said.

Rob just shook his head and handed me back the microphone.

"To your left is where the only known sighting of an *illegitimate* Yellowstone Sasquatch occurred—two actually. The hoaxsters, from

Idaho, or possibly Snap-Happy TV, were duly cited. And the fakery was fairly obvious, not because of any visible zipper on the gorilla suits mind you, but because of the accessories—a hard hat and lunch pail. You see, the two great apes then sat down right in the middle of a heard of grazing elk and started foraging—foraging around in their lunch buckets. I have the only known photo of them eating, by the way . . ."

The models' mouths all formed the word *banana*.

"Go on," Rob said to me, exasperated.

". . . but I sold the shot to the *Weekly World News*. It's just one of the reasons I no longer have to work for a living."

Rob sighed, "You might as well tell them the photo's caption."

"Gorillas in the Midst of a Meal."

"*Now* is it my turn?" Rob asked.

"Almost," I said to him and then to the passengers. "We're now nearing a military historical site. You see, from 1886 to 1916 the U.S. Cavalry was in charge of Yellowstone. And everywhere east of the area we'll soon be passing and south of the Gibbon River was used for the first ever war games held above 8,000 feet."

"Vait yust a minute dere, vasn't dat a Jogi episode too—'Missile Bound Bear?'"

"No, 'Missile Bound Bear' is a very special episode in which a crisis occurs for Boo Boo. It's when Yogi dressed his pal up as a queen bee, only to discover that the hollow tree they were attempting to rob contained Spanish fly instead of the anticipated Royal Jelly. Personally, I think the writers were all stoned."

And you'd think that if any one group of people would've known about that particular episode, it's a bunch of sweaty, Swedish guys wearing skimpy swim suits. But maybe something got lost in the translation.

"No, vee all tink dat vas episode tirdy-six, 'Royal Yellystone.'"

I then discovered that their stomachs weren't the only aspects of them that were revolting, as the mob inched closer to me—and my bag lunch.

"I think this is where I get off," I said to Rob as I backed toward the door.

And he gladly *let* me off—right there at the roadside—one small step for a park photographer, one giant 20 mile-per-hour *foof* for Scandihoovia. Uff da! If they only knew how close they came to causing an accident.

Photo Tips for the Faint of Heart

A s a longtime freelancer, one of the questions I'd most frequently be asked is: Have you *sold* a picture yet? This then
would almost always lead to a spirited debate, and the inevitable
follow-up question-of-semantics. But I should also mention that my
equally longtime penchant for antisemanticism is inherited from my
father's side of the family, so I'd usually just point out to Mom the
highly subjective nature of "fine art photography" before going elsewhere to field my next question.

What are the two greatest hazards to photo equipment today?

This I took to be a rhetorical question, since the camera bag sales-
man who asked it three years later seemed genuinely surprised at my
having such a ready reply:

"Poor eyesight," I said, "and pest control."

The issue here is that film manufacturers (back when there were
such things) would invariably recommend the loading of cameras
in subdued light. Common sense—right? Well you'd think so, but

this particular camera canon really should've had a built-in override function—an *un*common sensor. For instance, if it came down to a choice between changing your film (i.e. ASA) while hiding in a "Charo" brand butane-powered tanning booth, or in a dimly lit outhouse, an alarm would automatically go off, alerting you (and your high school guidance counselor), to go back and reevaluate the color and/or course of your paparazzo parachute, changing your *career* (ASAP) instead.

But if you just couldn't bear the thought of giving up photography, then you'd have probably wanted to veer toward the tanning booth to change out your film. You see, spare cartridges of *flypaper strips*, often found in celebrity outhouses (Robert Redford's for one), but less often in your average star-studded tanning salon, can look a lot like spare rolls of *35mm film* . . . and tend to gum up intricate film advance mechanisms. This (when combined with the more immediate hazard of, say, accidentally dropping your load-job off—to play with the less privileged Sundance "kids" at the cesspool)—easily exceeds the relatively minor risk of tanning booth bun burn.

Conversely, I've found that once every *blue* moon or so, I'm asked to comment on the perceived paranormal aspects of photography, even though editing software—enabling one to more closely match normal skin tones—has all but eclipsed this line of questioning. Nevertheless, I did receive one such query just the other night— from a Mr. R. Mapplethorpe.

Unable, though, to respond directly (my transmitting telepathy not what it used to be), I decided to relate one of my own mystical experiences here, and hope that "Bob" somehow has access to this essay on the "other side"—and that it helps him with his little exhibitionist exhibit over there.

The experience began with my being awakened by the sound of loud licking. Curiously, it occurred at the precise moment necessary for me to spring from the backseat of my '71 Pontiac and miss a spectacular shot of dawn's early light on Zion Canyon. It's what's known as *not* "making-the-scene"—or "scenic." And this particular instance of not "making-the-scene" was not only eerie, it was thought-provoking. It made me fully stop and think—but not necessarily in that order. For example, one might *first think* that a guy could have *then stopped* and at least put on some boxer shorts before missing the same exact shot, especially seeing as how even *sleeping* in the nude is a misdemeanor in Utah.

And I've since interpreted the licking sound to be either a Zionist plot, or a sign—or both. Like manna sent from heaven, mule deer with poor timing (and the gift of *rotary* tongues), came forth to clean my filthy vehicle—while also imparting a certain herd mentality. All reports, however, of a "feral adult" participating in a mini-stampede—or interspecies frolic of any kind—are purely anecdotal.

Of course the select few to whom I've told this story regard it simply as a sign that deer, in nationwide taste tests, unanimously prefer Bonnevilles—or at least ones that have recently been driven across their namesake salt flats. I, for one, attach much more significance to it and hereby call for controlled testing, perhaps using white rats and Tonka Trucks.

So many questions, yet so little time. Take for instance the question posed maybe twenty years ago now by my employer at the time, a Mr. A. Dolph Rhingbone. The distinguished Herr Rhingbone, as I respectfully addressed him (a real entrepreneur), owned a couple of Old West photo studios—you know, the ones where they dress customers in period-style clothing—and his question to me was:

> How on earth can a "bandito's" face be blurred beyond recognition, while the "bank teller's" sandals are in perfect focus?

I suppose it's a valid question, and apparently a popular topic, as several people asked me this—not just the detective down at police headquarters. And we've since come to find out that there is no clearcut answer, only inadmissible evidence.

There was some scant evidence, too, that Mr. Rhingbone once thought fairly highly of me, in that not long after I first started working there, he put me in charge of acquiring certain props for the studio. In fact, on a particularly slow day, as I agonized over the tedium, and put forth suggestions such as O.K. Corral shoot-out reenactments, and mortician slab scenes, it was Mr. Rhingbone himself who suggested that I go find a gun, ". . . und put yourzelf out of your misery."

"Jawohl, Herr Rhingbone!" I replied, clicking my heels and goose-stepping out the door (which, by the way, is really hard to do in sandals).

I returned roughly three hours later with my uncle's sawed-off twelve-gauge.

"He'll never know it's missing," I told a clearly disappointed Rhingbone. "It was hidden behind the ammonia tanks in his basement headquarters—next to some antisemantic literature."

The gun then quickly found a *new* basement home—the studio basement—hidden away for the meantime anyway, in the "spice" rack—next to the mace.

And although he found the slab scene a bit too morbid (at least ostensibly), Mr. Rhingbone wasn't always against my using a little imagination in a photo-shoot. He sometimes even encouraged it. So when a customer approached me about having his portrait taken and sent to his girlfriend in prison, my mind raced with inspiration. We ruled out a brothel setting, citing poor taste in this instance (she had "priors"), and saloon brawl (she had "priors"), and even a necktie party (too formal). And *I* rejected the, "premenstrual drag queen bitch-fest," theme—the customer perhaps having misunderstood the meaning of period-style clothing. But eventually, after reviewing some of the on-hand props, and later, some from the "dungeon" he and I finally came up with what we thought to be an appropriate theme.

"Nice shotgun," he said, fondling the six-inch barrels and breaking down the action, "real authentic."

Then, after giving me a long curious look, he asked if I knew that one of the chambers still housed a live round.

I confessed that I didn't, and in passing told him I'd take care of it if he'd just hand over the shell.

"Why? I'm not going to shoot you," he countered. "If everything goes well."

That's when we shared a brief nervous chuckle, *and* when I first came up with the idea for mental sticky-notes, making one at that particular point in time to pay closer attention to his, "ideas," one of which being to move the whole setup over to the cash register, to effect a more realistic-looking holdup scene.

Typecast as usual, I was forced to play the role of bank teller, but not before shrewdly thinking to secretly activate the self-timer device on the studio's camera as we walked by it.

Ironically, though, no small amount of non-mechanical—one might even say theatrical—timing, also played a role, as Mr. Rhingbone, right on cue, began barking his orders from the darkroom for me to get the previous day's hidden cash receipts ready for him to take to the bank. And at some point, I'm fairly certain during the Austrian entrepreneur's detailed instructions on just where to find them, the "candid" camera's shutter tripped—along with a perfectly synced but totally inexplicable fill flash—quietly creating exhibit "A" (as the police termed it).

Later, as I stood handcuffed at the doorway helplessly watching the getaway, and shouting, "Herr Rhingbone, Herr Rhingbone, Herr Rhingbone," a conscientious tourist from the sidewalk quickly diagnosed the situation and came to my rescue—nearly breaking some ribs in the process. Of course it wasn't exactly what I had in mind, but I'm sure ol' Doc Heimlich "Frontier Paramedic" would have approved of the technique.

And to my knowledge, the police still haven't caught the guy. Then again, my initial description of the suspect as wearing a sombrero, chaps, spurs, and a feathered boa, could have easily been considered a crank call, and probably didn't get the Deadwood Police Department's highest level of priority.

Furthermore, to answer Mr. Rhingbone's question about the

quality of the "customer's" exposed negative, I have only to say that a rapidly forming grin can sometimes cause a "bandito's" face to be blurred beyond recognition, not to mention the spot-metering problems caused by a glowing light bulb mysteriously appearing out of nowhere above said subject's head.

Come to think of it, many other queries arose concerning the possession of a sawed-off shotgun, but Mr. Rhingbone flat out denies its existence. He also denies once having a partnership with a Mr. R. Mapplethorpe, and having a dungeon with a spice rack. And I hear he's no longer fielding questions.

But I still am, although I'm limiting them now in terms of scope.

Some questions, of course, will continue to baffle. And these, of course, demand a higher level (or focal plane), of thoughtful consideration—perhaps even meditation. Why, for instance, would one strip of flypaper have little sprocket holes, and be totally ineffective to the exclusion of all others at catching flies? Why would a "non-period-style institution" even have an outhouse, or post guards outside the celebrity wing? Why do the restraints look so familiar? Could it all have something to do with my childhood and/or my relationship with my mother?

I've been contemplating these and other such mysteries for quite some time now (while cleaning the "advance gears" in my new Sony digital), and have come to the conclusion that I'd like all future questions to be photography related if you don't mind. Send them to: The Answer Man, care of the Smithsonian Institution, Washington D.C. I'll get to them as soon as they let me.

Kung Fool: On Parallel Thinking

The last will be first—except at a four-way stop. That, Grasshoppers, is my one and only argument for the separation of church and state. I think it's mine anyway—as much as anything can be. In any event, the saying came to me as my friend Lorraine (a known Catholic) parallel-parked her BMW in front of a Sikh Temple in Singapore City's Little India district—on a Sunday night. She always crosses herself (sometimes twice), before driving in Little India on a Sunday night. And the parking space in question was right across the street from a Hindu Mosque. We were there to pick up her husband Shawn—at a nearby Buddhist meditation center—before then going to a weekly gathering of radical Atheists.

Okay, I made that last part up. We were going shopping.

But the point is that there are a lot of religious people in Singapore—including Atheists I'm sure. And they all seemed to get along—except for possibly the Atheists. No one, at least as was my understanding, tried to make their religion first and foremost—except for possibly the Atheists. They used their respective religions to simply better themselves—with, of course, the possible exception of the Baptists.

I'll bet you thought I was going to say *Atheists* again didn't you?

And I wasn't a Baptist, or an Atheist, or even a Shaolin monk for that matter. But as a kid I did watch a TV show about a Shaolin monk, who after some problems arose in his native China, fled to the Old West, the American Old West, to search for his half-brother, who, no doubt, worked on the transcontinental railroad there. The monk's name was Kwai Chang Caine. And he wandered the American West in peace—at least until the producers of the show thought the scene needed a broken clavicle or two. Just before the violence, though, Caine would always have flashbacks to his training in the monastery, where his teacher—Master Po—would spew all kinds of wise sayings to his pupil. This helped Caine (or "Grasshopper" as Master Po called him), to kick some ass.

Caine was very inscrutable while kicking ass.

And that's how I thought everyone was in the Far East. But I'm somewhat naive. I get all my esoteric knowledge from TV shows like Kung Fu.

But it at least taught me how to *look* inscrutable. And I taught *myself* photography, taught myself photography in the American West, and even managed to forge a career in that field, one that eventually found me wandering the Far East looking very "scrutable"—a reverse Kwai Chang Caine if you will, with no producers, thank Krishna. I like my clavicles unbroken.

And I searched not for my half-brother, but for inspiration and perspective. You see, during the long dues-paying period of becoming a professional photographer, the long, long, *long* dues-paying period, I secretly wrote. In fact, I put more effort into my writing than my photography. I thought I was good too. And occasionally I'd get validation when I heard one of the "gags" I wrote being used on a first rate first run television program. It seems either the writers of *The Simpsons* stooped to my level; or *I* rose to *theirs*—an example of

19

parallel-thinking nonetheless. So I had to throw that particular "gag" out. No one would believe I didn't steal it. No big deal, though, I knew I could write more.

And I really needed to get away from TV and my protective bubble of the American West. I needed to leave my comfort zone and grow.

So Singapore it was.

But how are you going to tell the people with whom you're staying in Singapore, who so graciously opened their home to you, a comfort zone of it's own (with bubble *tea*), that you are there to "practice life" a la Kwai Chang Caine.

Shawn, for instance, might offhandedly ask you what you are going to do that day.

Will you then tell him that you are going to, "empty your mind?"

When Lorraine would later ask a similar question, would you then tell *her* that you're going to, "meditate your every action?"

No. You tell them you're going shopping. Because that's what people do there—normal people anyway.

And extreme shopping wasn't what I expected to experience upon my arrival in Singapore.

Instead of seeing wise men practicing Tai Chi on a rock in the river, I saw people drinking Chai Tea in a trendy café along the Riverwalk (at a place called the RiverWok). They all sat there reading the same self-help book too: *Ten Spiritual Principles to Help You Gain Material Riches*—or some variation on that title. Buddhist, Jedi, Hindu or Sikh—they all *sought* material wealth beyond their wildest dreams. Avarice seemed to be the only state-sponsored religion in Singapore.

Okay, there were exceptions. And before you think I'm being overly judgmental, I'm also not being totally forthright. I'm pandering to some extent—a foolish hypocrite pandering to those who might read this and still want to use some of their material wealth to buy my *next* book.

And as my empty mind slowly filled up with thoughts of sore feet (I'd been in the same spot in the same subway "practicing life" by letting people go ahead of me and getting nowhere—for hours), when I finally relented by having a seat and putting in my Ear Buds.

And did I listen to recordings of Master Po spewing wisdom? No, I listened to the David Feldman Radio Podcast of all things. My favorite storyteller—we'll just call him Dylan Brody Stevens—was David's guest that day, and he was, of course, telling a story, a story about parallel thinking while parallel parking.

Okay, I made that last part up. But he *was* telling a story.

And in this story I heard a familiar word. It was a made-up word—a clever made-up word—one that only Dylan Brody Stevens could make up. I take that back. *I made that word up too*—maybe twenty-five years ago—and put it in one of my own stories. In fact, I thought it was clever enough to have included it as part of a running "gag" throughout this entire book. Sure, I could throw that particular word out, but then I'd have to basically throw out the entire book, a labor of love on which I'd been laboring for over two decades.

My heart sank. But I continued listening. And later in that same Podcast, David Feldman (a known Jew), made a joke, a joke quite coincidentally I might add, about the actor who played Kwai Chang Caine in the TV series Kung Fu—an actor by the name of David Carradine. It had something to do with his having died (in a neighboring Asian country by the way)—of autoerotic asphyxiation. The joke, while funny I'm sure, had nothing to do with "gags" or gag writing, or gag-reflexes—even though it really should have. But it was the coincidence of it all that spurred me forward.

And after I once again emptied my mind (mainly of autoerotic asphyxiation thoughts), I walked—with great purpose now—to my cushy place at Shawn and Loraine's flat, where their high-speed, highly materialistic internet would allow me to research all of Master Po's wise sayings in hopes that one of them would help me with my perceived dilemma.

And this is what I found:

"The answer lies within you 'Grasshopper.'"

It didn't help me one bit. But I was right there at my laptop, so I started writing this particular story.

And as a longtime freelance *author*, one of the questions I'd most frequently get is: Yeah, but have you *sold* any of your writings? This then, would often lead to a spirited debate and the eventual follow-up question-of-semantics. And being a staunch anti*semantic* (a word Dylan Brody Stevens and I *both* thought of), I would often then change the subject.

"Who goes first at a twelve-way stop in Little India?" I asked Shawn, who was driving me around Little India that week.

"The first will be first," he said while crossing himself—twice.

That made sense, I thought, before *then* thinking some *more*. And what I thought about most was all the different religions and how their founders—transcendental figures in different parts of the world—who at different times in history all had at least some parallel thinking going on with each other. I further thought about how their teachings had been corrupted and modified and rationalized in order to help those who couldn't live up to them sleep at night.

But then again I probably think too much. We weren't on our way to church, we were on our way to go shopping. And this particular Kung Fool needed to buy some sleeping pills.

Malice Herbivorethought

Losing your first pet is always tough, unless, of course, he's a boll weevil. Then it's a piece of cake, or possibly even homemade cookies serving as the misplaced carcass' esopho-sarcophagus. And although more accurately an exoskeleton (bugs don't have carcasses), just the *thought* was pretty disgusting. If not immediately in my own large intestine, "Weevil Knievel," might have already been flushed, maybe as early as the previous morning—in a funeral not totally unlike those held for common Goldfish—common Goldfish *crackers*—and probably conducted by a single, largely indifferent survivor.

One can safely assume, too, that this burial en bulk had the same fundamentalist approach to pall-bearers as was employed a full five years later in my pet skink Earl's funeral—the little Velcro-toed lizard also a lightweight when it came to making friends. He had a special talent, though, for making enemies. Our 4th-grade music teacher, for instance, was so envious of Earl and his near perfect portrayal of the ornate handle to her top-left-hand desk drawer, that she subsequently staged an entire scene-stealing mini-production of her own (Handle's Messiah), often interacting extemporaneously, and operatically it would seem, with several imaginary cast members. Earl's insistence on always working alone, incidentally, may have even stemmed from this singularly spiteful display.

Neither of their careers lasted much longer I might add.

And although very low-maintenance animals by nature, *my* pets still managed to maintain a curiously high mortality rate. They regularly stopped working (alone or otherwise), not long after I gained custody.

Word, therefore, of this death wellspring quickly spread throughout the animal underworld—and ultimately leaped onto its own rocky shore of counterculture horror lore. To this "end" a long-haired subspecies of lemmings, having since abandoned their Burroughs (William S., and John), even rerouted their grim pilgrimage, in order to follow me—the head of the Grateful Dead pet set—home. And night crawlers, all hopped-up on nitrogen, would frequently conduct (so to speak), Kavorkianic back-alley deals with electricity, usually involving melancholic Beat Beetles and migrant swarms of lightning bugs.

Oh, it was a scene man—very bizarre—and very depressing. But eventually other—*less* suicidal—pets would also pick me; usually getting me sentenced to some big-time *time* in my girlfriend-of-the-month's doghouse.

"I couldn't shake him," would be my best response to her dubious look. "Can we keep him?"

"You're not even half picked over," she'd complain to herself while helping me out of my suet suit, a suit, by the way, designed especially for me—by her. "Hmm," she'd continue, "maybe if I'd lined the collar with bird seed, or . . ."

It's probably just as well, I thought, vulture cages are very hard to come by.

Ground-squirrel cages, on the other hand, look a lot like AMC

Pacers, and are (like my minimum-security relationships) based solely on the honor system.

And although the word *breakthrough* may be a tad strong, I am now able to admit to having once owned a Pacer. The world's first circular automobile, the Pacer sat mere millimeters off the ground, and consisted mostly of windshield. The interior, consequently, revolved around the adjoining dash. And that's where Manny resided—somewhere behind the cracked, contoured curvature of the car's spacious console. It was the ultimate in mobile habitat trails.

Manny (short for intake manifold), and I first met after coming out of a sharp turn on U.S. highway 287. It sounded as if an oblong tennis ball rolled from an area behind the oil light and came to an animated stop somewhere behind the glove compartment. Seconds later, an angry ground squirrel head emerged through the little open space by the accelerator pedal and began criticizing (in ground squirrel language), certain aspects of my driving, mainly those dealing with speed and cornering.

As a result, I did ease-up some—immediately. After all, it's perfectly natural to *de*celerate with both sandaled feet tucked neatly beneath your buttocks, a safe distance away from any small toothy animals well versed in surprise tactics. Over time, though, I got less jumpy and actually came to appreciate a ground squirrel looking up my right pant leg whenever he, in his proximate wisdom, deemed a tune-up or some other such maintenance operation necessary. (Only later did I learn that his brothers' names were Moe and Jack).

I got used to his choice of music too. He could somehow manipulate the radio from the back, locating Alvin and the Chipmunk songs at will. Just as mysteriously, all my brand-new Weird Al tapes were eaten. And anytime the mood struck, such as when he brought "home" a date, the Kasey Kaesem-dedicated "Ben" played.

Dates for the owner of an AMC Pacer were much more rare, unless, of course, you lived and worked in Yellowstone National Park. One such potential date might've even been the deciding factor in Manny's choice of living quarters, and thus, *my* new *title* of slumlord.

Most of the seasonal park employees, by way of explanation, arrive by way of bus, and therefore latch on to anyone possessing wheels—of any sort—even a "souped-down" prepossessed Pacer. Steve Levelle also had a vehicle, a nice one, but never wanted to drive the gas-guzzler. He would later elicit unflattering comparisons to Manny with regard to his freeloading, as well as his backseat driving. Molly, on the other hand, had very little in common with Manny, other than their mutual love of anything chocolate.

And to answer the age-old question of which came first—the girl or the squirrel—I'd have to flip a coin and say girl. Although Molly, while dining in the Pacer, once remarked that she thought that the little decorations on her brownies had turned rancid. "How long have these been in your car?" she'd ask.

"Decorations?"

"Yeah, the little chocolate sprinkles," she said, putting one to her tongue. "They're still edible though."

Molly was thus easily mollified, unlike so many of my previous female companions. That's what I liked most about her. And as long as I had ready access to chocolate desserts—my job there that year was as cook—she'd happily agree to ride with me all over the Yellowstone region.

"Baiting" the Pacer was also easy. I'd simply sneak some leftover dessert into the car before breakfast, while everyone was still sleeping. Then, after work, as Molly walked through the parking lot on her way to a trailhead, she'd suddenly stop and "sense" the chocolate in my car. I, of course, would already be behind the wheel, twirling my lucky rabbit's-foot key chain.

One time, as I waited in the Pacer for Molly, my supervisor walked by instead—having sensed a missing pan of Rococo Coco Nut-Bars (extravagantly decorated as the name would suggest). Quickly grabbing the plate of smuggled goods, I stashed it under the passenger-side seat, playing it cool until the heat died down. And, as it turned out, Molly just happened to have been a no-show anyway, having headed in the other direction that afternoon. So I completely forgot about the hidden desert—for days. And I assume that's how Manny first came to choose my car.

But I *know* why Steve Levelle did. He liked its wide ridicule radius.

"Maybe we should stop and wind the engine up again," he'd say as we labored up Craig Pass. "Did you bring the spare rubber bands?"

"Ha ha. Maybe we should take *your* car next time," I said, putting a brief halt to our witty repartee. "Did you bring any spare cash, for gas?"

After awhile, though, we ran into the inevitable bison traffic jam and Steve would impatiently reach over for the horn. Nothing.

"Doesn't *anything* work? Man, you really do need to trade this tin can in."

The horn, of course, did work. Manny just disconnected it because it tended to interfere with his pre-hibernatorial hypoglycemic stupors.

I also felt kind of guilty, incidentally, while driving outside of Yellowstone with Manny aboard, since Park regulations clearly prohibited the transfer of wildlife in and out of Wonderland. And it's not like I didn't try to evict him. I did—many times. But this master of mammalian-territorial-politics wasn't about to leave such posh accommodations, even when I wanted to be alone with Molly.

For example, one night, when Molly had momentarily left the car to "freshen up," I purposely held the cigarette lighter in for as long as I thought it would take to smoke the little voyeur out, which turned out to be very revealing—both psychologically and physiologically.

And it only succeeded in relocating the "third party" (temporarily), to the front of the engine compartment, where Molly, upon exiting the outhouse, caught her first real glimpse of Manny—encased in the head lamp.

Still "projecting," I hit the high beams, instantly producing his "skelhouette," as I like to call it, on the facility's outside wall. This, unfortunately (for me as well as Manny), constituted the rest of the night's entertainment—a crude but effective kinesiology lesson. Who knew, for instance, that a ground squirrel even had the "phalangicoidal" equivalent of a middle finger, or could extend it like that?

I therefore gave him the nickname—Flipper. And as expected, the very next morning I found my cigarette lighter (symbolically), missing from its socket.

Steve first met Manny in a more apt fashion.

"Ever change the oil in this tin can?" he'd ask as we crested a small hill and began the descent. "Oh, I forgot. You don't have to oil rubber bands. But you really should get the tension checked every thirty thousand miles."

Manny, who paid for as much gas, would have concurred, had he not been sleeping-off the effects of a late night of entertaining, cuddled up somewhere in the dash.

"Forget the rubber bands," Steve laughed. "I bet you got twin solar gyroscopes under the hood."

There was a brief pause as my *brain's* transmission shifted to overdrive.

"Actually," I explained, gaining momentum, "there's a treadmill under the hood. And I train small animals to run on it."

Steve continued laughing—only harder now.

"I'll prove it," I then said, making a sharper-than-what-*I'm*-even-used-to right-hand-turn onto Firehole Canyon Drive.

Immediately, the rolling oblong-tennis-ball sound could be heard—loud and clear—as if amplified somehow by the vacuum-sealed interior (which, by the way, is automatically created *whenever* two people simultaneously inhale what they think will be their last breath). The grumpy groundhog wannabe, his stupor rudely interrupted, then made his much anticipated (by me), appearance.

"Meet Manny," I said, regaining my composure. "Looks like there'll be six more weeks of summer."

And I'm guessing that it was out of shock, from careening on two wheels for the approximate time period of thirty seconds, or the eventual sight of an angry squirrel head popping through the open lighter socket, that Steve failed to utter so much as a single syllable for the rest of the ride home. And that gave me a chance.

"I'm thinking about taking on a marmot," I said. "More horse-power. And I hear they work for peanuts. But then I'd have to go to all the trouble of thinking up a name . . ."

This brought to mind my many previous childhood pets. Surely one of their names could be recycled. Let's see, I had thought of renaming my first pet Colin, after having eaten him—Small Colin. Hmm, how about Basil? No, that doesn't go with marmot. "What do you think Steve? Steve?"

Steve just kind of nodded.

But Basil would've only been a first name anyway. And come to think of it, an appropriate last name should've come to mind right away. Ah, but even I lacked the foresight to name a pet *Posthumously*. Maybe my next one.

Bluffing
(or Big Rock Candy Chickenheads)

EDITOR'S NOTE: There's a certain amount of rock climbing, mountaineering, and geological jargon that needs to be understood in order to better appreciate this chapter.

So to the uninitiated—here's a brief lexicon:

• "Rock!!!!!!": a shouted warning to anyone who might be climbing below you after you've accidentally dislodged a rock or stone.

• Chickenhead: a slang term for a protruding, jagged, easy-to-grasp handhold.

• Horn: an even larger, easy-to-grasp handhold.

• Jamming: a climbing technique whereby one places a body part (or one's entire body), into a crack in the rock. The climber then flexes that body part (or inhales), thus forming a tight seal between flesh and rock before theoretically continuing up the crack by repeating this process incrementally. Grabbing chickenheads is preferable.

• Chalk: a substance used to dry the sweat from a climber's hands, thus making it easier to climb. Blocks of chalk, also known as calcium carbonate, are stored in specially-made fleece bags that are attached to the back of a climber's harness. Calcium carbonate coincidentally (and maybe even ironically), is what makes up most kidney stones.

• Glenn Exum: an iconic climber and founder of the Exum Climbing School.

• Cragging: another word for *climbing*—*crag* being another word for *cliff.*

Got it? Okay, now back to our chapter:

Famed mountaineer Peter Lev and I were discussing our favorite conspiracy theory the other day, the one where we get together with the Bryce people and the Zionists to subvert the One-World Park Service Cabal, when *he* accidentally dropped a name. "Glenn!!!!" he shouted out afterward.

(Actually, the after*word* was: Exum! But that's another story altogether).

"No Peter," I admonished him. "'Glen' is what you yell after you drop a name while out hiking through a *meadow*. The generic name that you shout out after dropping a name while *cragging* is: Craig!" (Or Greg—no one below is going to worry about pronunciation. They'll be too busy ducking for cover).

It's too bad, though, that we were doing neither, instead, patronizing our favorite underground fast food joint, Burgerbuilders, where it's okay to name names, but only semi-acceptable to get drunk and randomly *shout* them out—to say nothing of admonishing people you hardly know.

"Who's he again?" Peter, nodding in my direction, asked his long-time friend David Reynolds.

David rolled his eyes sheepishly, "You know—the guy from Kansas . . . he was climbing with us this afternoon . . . led the third pitch?"

Peter strained to remember. "I got nothing."

". . . the one with all the corny puns and stories."

"Oh yeah," Peter then said rolling *his* eyes. "He followed us here?"

David looked away, embarrassed. He'd almost wished I'd never saved his life.

"Actually, I'm from Nebraska," I said, segueing into yet another story. "And it's a long drive from there to the Tetons. In fact, it's how I first met Cody Paulson."

They both then ducked for cover. But I followed them under the table, and—since I didn't drink—continued on with my story.

At the time, I was already a professional fog-walker. By that, I mean I walked around in an early morning fog, photographing objects therein. It's kind of a specialty of mine; or rather an "autistic technique" I'd developed over the years. And a handful of publishers paid me for the use of these foggy photos. I'd even earned the honorary title: The "Velvia Phog," partly from the many erroneous accounts of my being a University of Kansas grad (the van in which I lived at the time had a Jayhawk sticker on it when I bought it); and partly from the name I gave to the Astro Van, "Mr. Van Allen," whose Nebraska vanity plates were not nebulous, as some would say, they clearly read: NEBula.

But Cornstellations, Van Allen radiation "van" belts, legendary KU basketball coaches named Phog Allen, and even the phrase, "Peel me another ear of corn, NEBeulah," was beside the point, and much too obscure for this Nebraska farm boy. What I really needed was a new *title*, and therefore a new photographic challenge. Why not climbing photography?

And I didn't even know exactly where I was, other than being parked somewhere between Nebraska and the Tetons, my ultimate destination. Road weary, I just needed a place to crash for the night. Who'd have guessed, then, that that crash site would turn out to be a climbing destination in and of itself. And as usual, I woke up cornfused; still only a stones throw away from the banks of the Platte River. Was I awake, or "sleep-peeing?" The river never looked like that back home on the prairie.

"Kidney stone!" I then screamed out, never dreaming I'd get a response, other than an echo.

"Feel better?" came the calm (non-echoed), reply from below.

I quickly upzipped.

"Lucky thing for me I had my helmet on," the girl who would later introduce herself as *Dee* continued. "But thanks for the heads-up anyway. Just wish I'd had my earplugs in."

"And it wasn't even my usual-sized stone," I said by way of an apology.

Dee then began belaying her partner, Cody, while I resolved right then and there to cut back on the calcium supplements, and to possibly get a back-flow device installed.

"Watch out, it's a little wet here at the top," she advised Cody as he pulled the final piece of gear.

And despite our seemingly inauspicious start, Dee and Cody turned out to be my two favorite people with whom I've only spent about an hour conversing—maybe even my two favorite people period.

During that hour I related to them my many *fog*tography adventures (it's easy, for instance, when somnambulating in an early morning fog to nearly trip over sleeping Black Hills bison), and showed them some of my "autwork." They, in turn, shared with me their passion for raptors, which had me worried for awhile, until I saw some of their beautiful *bird* photography. You see, I thought for a second they might have been more of those stupid basketball fans (from Toronto)—or worse, paleontologists. (After all, I *had* just recently driven by a three-story outhouse, a three-story outhouse *built entirely from velociraptor fossils*).

But no, birds-of-prey were the order of the day, and just their hobby. Cody was at Fremont Canyon that week to teach a climbing course for the National Outdoor Leadership School, his nine-to-five. Dee tagged along, recovering from recent abdominal surgery. They both, though, had to be leaving—the students awaited—but promised to later pose for some climbing photos.

And I was thrilled at this generous offer, at least until Cody noticed the sticker on my van, and mentioned in passing his semi-familiarity with the KU athletic program.

"What's that chant the Kansas student-section does after every basketball victory?" Cody asked me. "How's it go—Raaaaww . . .?"

"I wouldn't know," I said, brusquely cutting him off. "It's kind of a sore subject."

But Dee and Cody weren't the only model climbers I met that day. Nat Patridge, after posing for me on a climb called Wine & Roses (section C in your climbing guidebook), handed me his Exum business card, and told me to look him up at the Teton Climbers' Ranch if I ever got around to it. This invite immediately triggered something in the C-Section of my *brain*—the coincidence section.

And whether you're mindful of it or not, we all have a C-Section. It's just that it's usually underutilized. Current research (conducted during various autistic fog-walks) shows that when you stop *over*-utilizing the other lobes of the brain (i.e. thinking), and start doing the things you love, you become more and more aware of the perpetual propinquities linking every*one* to every*thing*. Just how this *benefits* anyone or anything, is still being researched. But lately, I'd been seeing so many coincidences, so often, that I felt compelled to document them all, even grading them according to a decibel system I'd devised—thus demonstrating the above cognitive-under-utilization theory.

That Nat and his climbing partner, Adam, lived in or around Jackson Hole—my destination—qualified as only a class-IV coincidence. But already, I could tell that the day in general was shaping up as being special, something I hadn't seen since Blotte Montana, and wouldn't see again, perhaps, until visiting Synchronicity of Rocks in Idaho. And the "something" that Nat's polite words triggered in me, was the realization that the very day I'd decided to forgo fog-walking (you can somnambulate right off a cliff face if you're not careful) for *climbing* photography (you're usually tied in when nearly walking off a cliff), became the day climbers—good ones—came out of their Gore-Tex shells, and practically begged to be photographed.

And Fremont Canyon might be the best place for someone just getting started in climbing photography—not to mention for someone cultivating his or her first ever B.O. aura. You see, the North Platte River, before taking its long sabbatical through the great but featureless state of Nebraska, managed to carve one of the deepest, most narrow, most breathtakingly gorgeous gorges I'd ever seen. And because of this very narrow nature (nature, incidentally, that reveals a veritable vertical velociraptor graveyard), a person could stand on one side of the gap and actually hold a conversation with his or her subject on the other. So not a lot of preparation or rigging is necessary—for the photos. Bathing, however (in the river below, or anywhere else on primitive BLM land for that matter), takes at least three full semesters of logistics training, and is therefore relatively easy to neglect.

And all went well for this beginner. I'd even run out of film, exposing all my outdated 4x5 Ektachrome sheets on Cody and his almost effortless lead of a climb called Dillingham Blues. Likewise, my *personal* emulsions were developing quite nicely, the "all-day" deodorant barrier having recently been breached. So after scratching and sniffing (each armpit), in dramatic fashion (and mentally measuring the progress), I put my camera gear safely away in Mr. Van Allen, and rejoined Cody on his side of the canyon. And I got there just in time to once again see Dee's face appear at the lip of the ravine. ("Deejà" vu.)

"I almost didn't recognize you with your fly closed," she said. "And you know, my ears are *still* ringing from that shout-out of yours."

"Would you like to give it a go?" Cody then asked referring to the climb.

"I don't know . . ." I hemmed.

"But you already have your climbing shoes laced up," Dee said, encouraging me. "Come on."

"How hard is it?" I asked.

"Not hard," she said apparently estimating the answer by the number of popped stitches in her abacus abs. "I hardly felt a thing."

I'd meant, *what grade was it rated*, but got the distinct impression that they didn't pay much attention to such things as ratings and grades. And, hey, I'd only be top-roping. So what the heck. How hard could it be?

And to be honest I was anxious to give it a try, so anxious I'd forgotten to load my chalk bag. But as it turns out, the rock face *itself* could have been comprised entirely of chalk and it wouldn't have made much of a difference—maybe accounting for one less leg-quiver, and/or one cubic inch off the odor aura.

And it was only after a full thirty seconds into my attempt at jamming up the this evil off-width crack, that I started fantasizing—fantasizing about ledges and hand holds to be exact. At one point I even had visions of large chalk chickenheads—large chalk chickenheads attached to talcum powder horns.

But the chickenheads were what mostly stood out in my fantasies. Because just like the proverbial phledgling chicken hawk stalking Phoghorn Leghorn (a heady enterprise in itself), this now-even-more-fowl-smelling little would-be pullet-puller never stood a chance. Style points, a corncept somewhat foreign to me anyway, became increasingly incomprehensible as I repeatedly jammed and fell, a sweaty worm wiggling on the end of a rope ten feet above the emerald river.

Fantasy then naturally gave way to prayer, as I prayed for the giant sturgeon that would surface and put me out of my misery. And the only positive to be gleaned from it all, I thought, might have been the knowledge that I dangled under the lone auspices of Dee and Cody.

Anyone else would have made fun of my flailing.

"Ever think of *swimming* back home?" Dee shouted down at me. "Where's my knife—and my soap? Phew! I can smell you all the way up here."

(*Taunting*, I've since learned, is technically not the same as *making fun*.)

"At least this gives us a chance to practice our rescue techniques!" Cody then yelled down. "You don't mind if the class watches, do you?"

I think I nodded *yes*, but the class all gathered around nonetheless.

"He'd have flashed this by now if he had some chalk," Dee told the class before tossing a large chip off her block in my direction.

"Rock!" one of the students absentmindedly yelled down.

"She means 'chalk!'" Dee loudly corrected.

Right on cue, a large bird then flew overhead and another student—sucking up to the teacher—yelled, "Hawk!"

And we didn't have to wait long for the echoed refrain.

"That's it!" Cody said as he pulled me up another three inches. "That's the Kansas Jayhawk chant: Rawwwk . . . Chawwwk . . . Jayyyy . . . Hawwwk!"

The class all began to chant as well—the resultant din all too phoggen reminiscent of Allen Fieldhouse. And I couldn't see it at the time, but Dee and Cody were also "reading the flight" of the red-tailed hawk as it soared overhead.

"It all augurs well for you, my friend," Cody continued as he reeled "Stinkbait" in the rest of the way. "The hawk tells me that you'll never make the cover of *Rock & Ice*; but your photo of me will."

And a little research into the back issues of that fine publication will tell the reader all he or she needs to know about the "science" of auspreyology—or in other words, the discovery of omens by observing raptor flight-patterns. It'll tell you that it's completely for the birds.

Then the other group of students, the ones on a paleontology field trip from Lawrence Kansas, who'd noticed my van's sticker—and the chanting—came over to introduce themselves. This, of course, totally blew my mind—the resultant head gasket failure causing a cog in my cognition to drop and bounce over the cliff edge. So I instinctively yelled out something like, "*whatever*," and classified the coincidence as a "5.11b."

"Wait a minute, aren't *you* from Kansas?" Dee, who was still unthinkingly doing what she loved best—(taunting me), asked. "What a small world."

"Yeah," Cody said. "It reminds me of the time Paul Petzoldt and I . . ."

"Craig!" I then yelled out all too soberly.

But it got David and Peter to stir. And it seems they'd only heard bits and pieces of the above story that I'd been telling them, mainly the bits and pieces about the one-*small*-world order of fries.

"Did you say Nat Patridge," Peter then asked, before turning sentimental and looking back at David? "He's one of my best men. We should really use him to infiltrate the Big Wall Zionists down there in Utah."

David nodded, then nodded back out. Neither would remember a thing, I thought, as I rolled them over onto their stomachs. So it'd be up to me to remind them how I saved them both from drowning on their own vomit. But that's another story altogether.

The 50-Year-Old Mile High Virgin

That's right. Fifty years had come and gone and I'd never done anything risqué on a commercial airliner. But that's only because I'd never *been* on one. Oh I'd practiced, don't get me wrong, in what's known as the poor-man's flight simulator. I even brought the flight handbook, or what I took to be the flight handbook, a well worn copy of *Coffee, Tea or Me* into the Greyhound bus' lavatory. I figured it'd be better to start by soloing in this case. I'd work my way up to an inflatable stewardess for the real flight.

But I doubted any such mile-high club's membership committee would count that as a real hook-up anyway. So as I sat, my "mile hymen" fully intact, in my first commercial airline seat, prior to my first commercial takeoff—the first commercial announcement came on over the loudspeaker. It had something to do with SkyMall and duty free stuff. But then another voice came on:

This is your Captain speaking . . . just a reminder that it is the policy of this airline to prosecute to the fullest extent of the law anyone harassing the flight staff in any way. And this means you—yeah, you holding the *Coffee Tea or Me* book! So I think I speak for the entire crew by saying, somewhat sarcastically of course, that we hope you enjoy your first flight. And as always we thank you for choosing Virgin Airlines."

That's what *I* heard anyway—unnerving even *if* only partly imagined.

But the next thing I heard was a *real* shocker, and I didn't imagine it. It came from the armrest hog in the isle seat to my immediate right who'd noticed the book on my lap.

"You know, believe it or not, that book is a very realistic portrayal of the airline business in the 1960's and early 70's—it's entirely true."

No way, I thought, before expressing my astonishment to him.

"You actually *read* the book?"

Then a late-boarding passenger—an extremely attractive dead-ringer-for-one-of-the-cheesiest-of-the-cheesecake-like-illustrations-in-the-book late-boarding passenger—stowed her hand luggage, and politely crawled over Armrest Hog and me to her seat by the window. "Whew, I almost missed the flight," she said. And then, after getting situated, catching her breath, and noticing my total fascination with the seat pocket in front of me—and all its contents, "Oh, I'm sorry. Would you like me to read the safety instructions to you?"

"I'm uh, I'm not special—if that's what you were thinking," I replied. "I uh . . . it's just that I've never been in a plane before and everything's all so new to me and . . ."

"Wow," she interrupted, "that must be a very embarrassing thing to confess—you know, given your advanced age and all."

Now I must say that I actually could have passed for forty (at a time when forty was the new thirty). And while to her, forty is still "advanced," that's not the point of the story. The point is that when your mind is in a perpetual holding pattern (somewhere over 1972), and your body is sitting between two people, one who has just confirmed your beliefs that everything in your flight "Bible,"

Coffee, Tea or Me is entirely true, including I have to assume (since I didn't read it), the illustrations, illustrations depicting airplanes as the extremely effective networking tools for dirty old men hooking up with voluptuous young ladies; the other a voluptuous young lady, then you really don't need a point—anymore than *Penthouse* really needs proper sentence structure in any of the letters it receives.

It doesn't help that when after the plane eventually gets in the air your flight attendant, Gerald, offers you coffee, tea, or Cherry Coke at the approximate time your ears pop and Voluptuous Girl gives you her name and a confession of her own—that *she's* never had *sex* before—anywhere.

It further complicates matters when she goes on to tell you (as if anything else had any meaning whatsoever at that point in your life), that she'd recently been graduated from massage college and was currently on her way to an internship in Singapore, the same Singapore, coincidentally, to which *you're* headed for the sole purpose of getting your very first professional *massage*.

The onslaught of offhand in-flight info continues, as Armrest Hog, who's overheard everything, informs us that Voluptuous Girl's name—Trudy—is ("believe it or not"), the same as that of one of the main characters in the already way too referenced book, *Coffee, Tea or Me*.

And to this *day* I'm not sure I was able to fully take in *all* of the above. But I did manage to take it all *in stride*. And I'm proud so say I had the correct response to everyone involved, which is respectively:

1) "Cherry Coke please."
2) "Never?"
3) "Massage college. That's weird—*I've* never had a professional *massage* before." and;
4) "You actually *read* the book? Really?"

And here's where certain missives to certain publications might say that "this is where it gets interesting." But *they're* all fiction. My article is 100% exaggerated fact-based. *It* only gets less interesting.

The *Penthouse* letter, of course, has a pimply-faced 20-year-old first-timer reading this particular article (as first published perhaps in Hooter Airline's in-flight magazine), when a voluptuous older lady squeezes into the adjacent seat. Coincidentally both *their* names are Trudy too and they're eventually escorted to the lavatory by their flight attendant Geraldine (a little person in orange hot pants), who eventually joins them.

Fact based article, however, has the male protagonist (me), getting Trudy's signature on a quickly drawn up affidavit stating her lack of affiliation with any known airline in any known universe, and being interrupted as usual by Armrest Hog, who, as it turns out, just so happens to be a notary public. Trudy then escorts the protagonist to the lavatory—although she does this in much the same way any good Girl Scout might escort some confused elderly person who'd never been in an airplane before, and only offers to hold his, *"handbook"* while she waits outside.

When Trudy later finishes her recital of how many different kinds of massage she's qualified to administer the protagonist notices that none of the techniques include the words *exotic* or *sensual* and suddenly snaps out of his third-person reverie.

And so as *I* remained seated and buckled into *my* first commercial airline seat, just prior to my first commercial descent—into my first foreign country—my now fully popped eardrums processed the final commercial announcement of the flight. It had something to do with SkyMall and duty free stuff. But then another voice came on over the loudspeaker:

This is your captain speaking. The temperature at Singapore's Changi International Airport is a balmy seventy-eight degrees Fahrenheit, twenty degrees Celsius. And just to remind you, for the sake of expedience please fill out your immigration forms before entering customs. If at that time you still have anything to declare such as coffee, tea, or your disbelief in all things published back in the decadent nineteen-seventies, friendly customs officials will be standing by to confiscate the book, rip it to shreds, and give you a nice relaxing neck rub. We sincerely hope you enjoyed your flight, and as always we thank you for choosing Abstinence Air.

But then again, that's just what *I* heard.

Cursin' "It"

"**K**eep your hands where I can see them!"
These eight-little-words, usually heard *during* a date—not prior to one—were nevertheless the order of the day (if not the entire summer), as they rang out from the ranger car's loudspeaker.

So I extended my arms through my already open driver's-side window and without further prompting from "Mr. Microphone" slowly opened the door of my vintage Ford Tourette from the outside. It's the only way it *would* open, of course; a minor point, albeit one on which other former owners of such vehicles will all loudly—and quite colorfully—back me up, I'm sure.

And I'm guessing the *unit* backups whose own hands gripped various automatic and semi-automatic weapons, already had some of my other—more vital—body parts (autonomic and semi-autonomic), in their *sights*. Their best guess (while we're all guessing), I'm guessing, must have been that the "suspect" (me), merely had the whole "opening-of-the-door-from-the-outside" part of the "routine" down pat.

But moments later after seemingly also presuming to assume the pat *down* position—the face-to-the-ground fingers intertwined-behind-the-head submission-type-pat-down position, it came to me—why I was being detained, that is. It came to me with obsidian clarity. And I'm not sure, but I think "it" traveled through the medium of light—an inexplicable brilliant flash of white light.

I then felt the urge to share this revelation of mine, to testify if you will, to anyone who might be interested, even though the ranger straddling me—her one hand clutching the $4,000 grubstake (once wadded in my right front pant pocket), the index finger of her other wiping a powdery substance from the region of my left back pocket—strongly advised against this testimony.

"Damn-ass-cuss!" I nevertheless said—for starters—despite being a good fifteen feet from my Tourette.

But I don't think any of "it" (no matter how you define it), would ever have been held against me in court—considering my dissociated state at the time. For that matter, I also have my doubts that any of the on-hand rangers possessed the necessary talents or "gifts" needed to interpret even a small portion of the *car*ismatic crap this borderline "asthmatic chap" (an alternater ego), might have uttered about roads, health inspections, the burgeoning belay-slave trade, borders, lines, crack, potholes, plot holes, crackpot holes, plastic-puke-portals, or any of the other, less-conventional, urpin' legends at that time involuntarily issuing from my flesh-and-blood blow hole.

And apparently, the flash of light, which caused something like scales to fall from my eyes, is what triggered the first flash*back*—to the previous winter:

"When did you start wearing *hard* contacts?" my optometrist asked while looking through a jaundiced (Eyefocal brand) contact lens (my left one to be exact).

"Right around July," I replied, before explaining to her the necessity of hiking open-eyed through steamy mineral-infused backcountry thermal basins. "They started *out* soft."

"I see," she said icily. "And let me guess. You hike open-*mouthed* too."

"It's probably the sulfides in the steam . . ." I said through clenched, jaundiced *teeth*.

(A Mr. Quincy Magoo, having then taken over my body, resisted the urge to ask her why she thought they called it *Yellow*stone. And why she didn't leave the dental opinions to qualified dentists).

She then ratcheted the wrist straps even tighter to the chair, in turn triggering my *mind's* eye to dilate and get all blurry with further (more relevant), revelation—a flash *forward* this time, *back to the summer*, when I was working in Yellowstone—but still prior to the arrest:

I saw myself slipping surreptitiously into the walk-in freezer with a spray-bottle full of Yellowstone tap water, and an equally murky purpose. I then suddenly felt what others have described to me variously as a pang of conscience and/or semi-unconsciousness—the antiquated cast-iron meat-hooks hanging head-level, in a very impractical place. But not to worry, the pangs didn't last.

And Joe wouldn't need his *arm*, "the real me" reasoned while returning to the task at hand. After all, the CPR class practices by pounding Joe's sunken, rubberized *chest*, and sucking Joe's fake, government-issue *face*. And besides, one of my other, more responsible personalities (Dr. Jekyll perhaps), would no-doubt return the arm to Joe right after the government health inspection—long before the next CPR class. In other words, I stole a Park Service CPR dummy's arm (the early models had actual limbs), for some nefarious reason and was placing it (for the same reason), in a walk-in freezer.

And the trick was in keeping Joe's sprayed-on forearm-ice thin enough for the health inspector to be able to see through it to the requisite label and date—(keeping in mind that this was roughly the *same* date *Jeffrey Dahmer* was keeping a stiff upper-lip in court). The hand obviously also had to be visible, perhaps palming a stainless-steel freezer thermometer. Icicles on the fingertips were to be added last—an ice touch, so to speak. And a container labeled "ghoul-ash" would eventually be stored nearby.

Hey, who said managing one of Old Faithful Village's Employee Dining Rooms, didn't require certain skills, and/or a working knowledge of human anatomy?

It's too bad, though, that I wouldn't be there to witness the consequences of my practical joke, my two days off undoubtedly to coincide with the lady health inspector's upcoming visit. Oh well, at least I'd have the satisfaction of knowing, second *hand*, that she'd never again ambiguously ask me to keep my meat hooks sanitized and where she could see them.

And the flashback continued to flash forward—to one of those very days off—but still prior to the arrest:

"Why can't *I* wear the store-bought harness," my neophyte climbing partner complained as I fashioned my trademarked Mountain-Mummy™ homemade-sit-harness all around her rather supercallipygeocious mummy-parts?

My homemade harness, by the way (aka the Belay-Slave™), is really just a bunch of slings tied together, but I froze in mid-ring-bend and scratched my knotted head at her question. To me, *store-bought* was an uncertain term.

And what you'd think "Daisy Mae" would've already known, being from the South, is that only as the Belay-Slave's *owner* is one allowed certain uncertain terms, or slanglage (past tense plural sling-language), to be precise. *First Crack* (as it applies to climbing etiquette), not to mention *Mountain-Mummy* and *supercallipygeocious*, are indeed all fully registered to me. So is *Chimney Sweep* for that matter. Hey, it's good to be the royal wordsmith.

But it's even better to be "The Tailor" (an alterator ego). *He* now only needed to take the Mountain Mummy in a little in front. And in doing just that (by cinching the "crotch loop" up to the "waist belt" with a finder's-piece carabiner), his sore, mineral-coated eyes, suddenly fell upon her expialibodacious *upper* development.

"Uh . . . you'll be needing a Tailor Maid™ chest-harness too," the "Taylor" said.

"And don't climbers usually have special bags to hold their chalk," she asked?

I could also trademark a tape gag, I thought, before remembering my minimalist approach to climbing, which included a boycott of such accoutrement as tape and bags—at least until the various dealers came down in their prices.

"Why yes," I finally answered with a poetic pun, "*butt* you'll just have to dip your digits in my back pocket 'til I get one."

Done. And later, as "The Tailor" began the process of sweeping away inseam chalk lines—"it" hit me. It hit me with pure uncut calcium carbonate clarity. *She*, of course, claimed that a mosquito had landed on my cheek. *I* still don't believe her. After all, who kills mosquitoes with their fist? And I'm not sure, but I think *it*, or the memory of *it*, combined with the white cloud of chalk dust enveloping my head, is what caused me to flash forward yet another forty or so minutes:

"Damn-ass-cuss!" I had a date with Destiny and was running late. And believe me, Destiny DeTestemè (not her real name), *wasn't* one for excuses, expressed in tongues or otherwise. Nevertheless, I was still making decent time. I'd just dropped my climbing partner off at the clinic—to get her sprained fist looked at—having long since crossed the Teton borderline with *her*, and was already blowin' on down the Road to Perdition (or Colter's Hell as Yellowstone used to be called)—when I noticed the first ranger car.

The place had been swarming with *un*marked ranger cars the day before. But that, I figured, was merely a part of their ongoing efforts to frame me. I was used to it. You see, for years Dogface & The Fur King (undercover rangers posing as Mountain Man Rendezvousers— or more likely just a coupla' Geyser Gazer volunteers)—had been trying to get me banished from the area, or at least branded a crackpot by planting "geyser-soap" on my person.

Soap, or detergent of any kind, as any park "insider" can tell you, will temporarily turn a normally placid hot spring into a fully active geyser—probably by disrupting the surface tension of the hot spring—and definitely destroying its natural state in the process. It's very illegal, very stupid, and I'd never be a proponent—let alone an intentional user. But, as previously mentioned, I have, in fact, found "inexplicable" little sample soaps, and even full-sized bars, planted in my daypack just prior to planned hikes to various backcountry thermal features—Irish Spring being two examples in one.

But this soap-conspiracy was relatively harmless, *and* lightweight, so I managed to take most of it in stride. On one of my *less*-tolerant days, though, upon finding a piece of the mysterious quasi-contraband masquerading as bear bells hanging off my backpack, I snapped, and just hammer-tossed the phony evidence as far as I could, in a wonderfully-therapeutic purge of righteous indignation. And although I did *feel* better, I also quickly came to the obvious realization that one can't swing (or fling), an 11-mil. (or even 9.5-*milled*), soap-on-a-rope anywhere in Yellowstone Park without hitting *some* sort of once-dormant pool.

Looking back, I'm now almost ready to concede that this whole "soap-setup" scenario might merely have been a manifestation of the Industrial Surfactant Persecution Complex from which I suffer at times. Or it might have been just a few rogue coworkers (a conspiracy nonetheless, one quite possibly involving my roommate), who assembled, or *were* assembled, for the express purpose of providing subtle hints to me vis-à-vis my perceived Hobbit-like habits of personal hygiene. Or a combination of both. And as always, the possibility does still exist that the Amway corporation really *was* involved.

But *this* was *different*. No covert ops or shady pyramid schemes here. It was a fully-marked ranger car that was following me.

"Damn! Ass! Cuss!" "The Fugitive" said, as a chunk of his Ford Tourette fell off and disappeared into a deep cavernous fissure. A second ranger car then caught up to the first one, and without thinking,

"The Fugitive" swerved into the other lane to avoid yet another of these deep cavernous potholes.

And the only reason I could maneuver like that was because of the complete lack of any tourist traffic—which really had me worried. Here it was, a brisk September late-afternoon, dusk ordinarily merging with the outflow of locals and an occasional inbound tour bus. But dusk now had only sulfurous vapor clouds with which to commingle. And to make a lung story short, some of this dusk, a lot of those vapor clouds, and even some of "Daisy Mae's" calcium carbonate all got together for a clandestine meeting—in "Borderline Asthmatic Chap's" bronchial passageways. So I was definitely in no shape to blow on any gosh darn Breathalyzer.

Then a third cruiser's siren began to wail and before you could say the word *graft* the ranger was on top of me putting my life's-savings back *in* my front pocket. She stopped just short, however, of placing the aforementioned index finger (the one which had wiped the powdery substance from my back pant pocket)—to her tongue.

And in between my own breathless utterances, "Fur King this, and Fur King that," I *overheard* a few choice morsels—mostly, "Cache" this, and "cut" that—and "fencing stolen *arm*aments" this, and, "he looks stupid enough" that. And, if that wasn't enough, there may have even been some mention of cardiopulmonary resuscitation during their discussion of whether or not to cuff me.

But fortunately one of the rangers recognized me—Ranger Smythe.

"They call him 'The Wheeze'—among many other things," he said. "I actually know him. He's fairly harmless."

And apparently I didn't fit the physical description either, because the ranger in charge then apologized and explained that they were looking for a more-cinematic-like fugitive, possibly one with some sort of prosthesis, who might have iced someone. He too drove a Tourette, and was thought to be hiding in the area. And have I seen anything like that?

"Uh . . ."

"Sir, you mentioned something about fake vomit, in between your 'furking' comments?"

"Uh . . ."

"We have reason to believe the real suspect is also connected to a theft," the ranger continued, "a local theft involving the limbs of a government-issue Park Service CPR dummy. And he may have left what we in the 'business' call a signature calling card . . . or what we in the 'calling' call a signature business card. I get those mixed up."

"Huh . . .?"

Ranger *Kimble* then continued,

"He made G.I. Joe blow! With fake vomit! That's how sick he apparently is. And if we weren't so busy with this murder-larceny thing," she warned me (eyeing the evidentiary blood on my hands), "we'd book you for attempting to climb Obsidian Cliff."

One of the many other rangers then "dispersed and disassembled" a blurry (to me anyway), elderly couple wearing what appeared to be his-and-her moose hats (*his* with antlers—*her's* just a beanie). They spoke with a German accent and had somehow managed to breach the blockade.

"Move along. There's nothing to see here!" the ranger said.

One of the two—the "bull" I think—who, for what it's worth, smelled of peppermint hemp oil—thought differently, and managed to get off one additional flash photograph for their home slide show—or for some *other* reason perhaps.

At that point my eyes rolled back up into my head, as this second brilliant flash of white light elicited even more elucidation, and triggered a trance state that lasted well into the night—and my date with Destiny:

"Who programmed you?" Destiny demanded incredulously.

"It was Dogface & The Fur King," "The Leather Chap" said, no longer believing the two mystery-men to be undercover rangers. "I swear! Every time a camera flash goes off, so do I."

And it would've been pointless to mention the possible Dr. Bronner connection. So I didn't. I just laid there, as usual, in the automatically-assumed submission-type position.

"And I suppose they gave you *that* too," she said, a stiletto heel hovering ominously over four slightly-off-color depressions in the left side of my face.

"The Chap" stroked the depressions with his fingers and pondered the moment. It was definitely a "white knuckler," *and* kind of a strange discussion for a campfire—even a *drive-by* campfire. Ghost stories would have been much more appropriate. Something like: Who Stole My Arm?, or: The Ghost of Bloody Finger Cracks.

And "The Slave" (not to be confused with the Belay-Slave™), of course couldn't help but chime in, mumbling something to this effect—programmed alternator egos being what they are.

"How 'bout: The Dirtbag Joker Who Spoke in *Pierced* Tongues?" Destiny offered, brandishing a sharp firebrand stick in the direction of the immobilized slave. "Or, Auto Erotic Asphyxiation," she continued—coughing—and trying unsuccessfully to roll up the window of the smoke-filled auto, before then leaving in a huff.

"Or, The Hook," The Wheeze called out after her, hopefully?

And if I remember my campfire stories correctly, hanging from the passenger-side door handle of my Ford Tourette would be a thoroughly scrubbed and sanitized meat-hook. Damn-ass-cuss! Even that wouldn't get me off—the hook. But it does help to realize that health inspectresses know "the routine" too, and aren't without a sense of humor after all.

Up Wickiup Creek

I looked up the word *wickiup* in the Wikipedia the other day and found a small poxvirus attacking my PC—a "pox Americana" bug to be exact. And it really put a crimp in my research. The Wikipedia, for those of you who don't know, is a free online reference site that anyone can add to or edit—anyone with serious intentions that is, and a lot of anti-virus software. (The people at Wikipedia don't kid around). So it's a good thing I had all my notes saved to disk prior to my first all too tongue-in-cheek attempt at contributing to this website. And after a quick trip to Software City, I felt as ready as ever for yet another try at getting published.

My subject: the 1869 Folsom-Cook-Peterson (FCP) expedition to the source of the Yellowstone River. My qualifications for writing it: none—unless you count being the possessor of some little-known but very relevant historical documents a qualification. These documents will hereby be known as the Peterson letters.

William Peterson (the P of FCP)—a great, great, great uncle after whom, as far as anyone knows, I was middle-named—is often over-looked by such noted Yellowstone historians as Aubrey L. Haynes and Lee H. Whittlesey. Packers, cooks, and even the dogs on the Washburn expedition get more publicity than Uncle Willie. And for good reason—Willie had the reputation for being a malingering, bestial, ne'er-do-well recreant of the worst kind. Even among present-day relatives he's the great, great, great uncle about whom nobody talks. And that could be why the letters had remained hidden for so many years.

But in the interest of revisionist history I have now managed to set the record straight, and all anyone has to do to view it is to search the *Wicca*pedia website (the folks at Wikipedia still refuse to recognize great writing and have had a pox put on them and their homepages by the fine people at Wiccapedia). Or you could just read the transcribed entry below:

THE PETERSON-COOK-FOLSOM
EXPEDITION

The Peterson-Cook-Folsom expedition of 1869 is widely regarded to be the first organized party to explore the Yellowstone headwaters, their sole purpose being to share their findings with science. Originally, the assemblage consisted of as many as 13 men, but 10 of them dropped out, citing, as Cook puts it, "a fondness for his hair." In fact, according to Mr. Cook's somewhat over-publicized diary, the group's departure on Sept. 6th from Diamond City (near Helena), was met with their would-be-explorer friends' "parting salutations" of: "If you get into a scrap, remember I warned you . . . and, if you get back at all you will come on foot . . . and, it is the next thing to suicide, etc., etc." The Peterson letters, however, mention no such send-off and even had the three departing under the cover of darkness, their *gold pans* (and other such geological equipment), under the cover of blankets.

After obtaining provisions in Bozeman the three continued south via the old miners' route, eventually reaching
the Yellowstone River near Emigrant Gulch. According to
the Folsom-Cook article (published in the July 1870 issue
of Western Monthly), on the eighth day out they, ". . . encountered a band of Indians, who proved to be Tonkeys, or
Sheepeaters, and friendly . . . the discovery of their character greatly relieving our minds of apprehension . . ."

But the Peterson letters go into greater detail, describing the Sheepeaters, at first anyway, as flower-loving,
lacto-ovarian vegetarian nature worshipers, and kindred
conscientious objectors. They dealt primarily in odd notions and strange potions. These "Amish equivalents," as
they'd been depicted by various fur trappers of the day,
even refused to adopt the horse as a means of transportation. Peterson, at home with their general laissez-faire phi-
losophy, secretly hoped they had no such adoption policy
for lazy-fair-haired Swedes like him. He wanted in.

And while the Folsom-Cook account then starts to veer
away from matters anthropological (to fixate instead on
physical concerns), the Peterson letters go on to describe,
much more fully, the tribe and their mysterious ways. The
Sheepeater (or Tonkey), with the best English skills even
took an enthusiastic Peterson on a walking-tour of their
empire, which included showing him the sheep snares
and the hot springs they used to "relax" the rams horns.
The straightened horns (odd notions), were then made
into a unique type of crossbow, and sold (along with obsidian arrowheads), to the military industrial Crow complex. Peterson's extreme disappointment at these findings
is henceforth reflected in his later correspondence. It's
thought that it was either the literalness of the horn-un-
curling thing, the hard work, or the hypocrisy of it all that
soured him so.

They then returned to the shared (i.e. communal), camp where Peterson found some Sheepeater children teaching Messrs. Folsom and Cook a game played with a type of foot bag (also made from sheep), the object of which being to stand in a circle (made around a pentagram), and kick the bag so as to keep it from touching the ground. These foot bags were also used as a sort of sachet, filled with arnica-flower and camas flour (strange potion), that effectively treated their acne, or their hacknee—the language barrier causing no small amount of confusion.

Likewise, they found that the tribe's name (an apparent misnomer), actually originated from the very first ramshorn crossbow that they marketed, the semi-automatic rapid-fire Sheepeater model—and not as some might have inferred, from any sick, twisted reason Peterson may have imagined at one time.

And the confusion continued later that night inside the main wickiup when Folsom carelessly dipped his sole bargaining chip into the ceremonial "barter starter," breaking it in half—and in turn nearly breaking off trade negotiations. This unfortunate faux pas instantly drew a dubious stare from the chief, who strongly suspected that the outsiders had way more than the host's own appetizers to offer. And apparently in the chief's culture it wasn't polite (or healthy), to put consumables into the sheep dip (his very own copyrighted recipe), until after the dealing was done.

In the end, however, it turns out that one semi-automatic sheepeating crossbow; a couple of Tonkey (or Tatonka), toys; and various other odd notions of Americana thrown in for good measure, is a pretty fair trade for a useless (as they by then realized), gold pan; Peterson's reserve hipflask; and some musty old blankets—*pro*viral software to be traded to neighboring tribes.

The chief, after his wife emptied the remainder of the sourdough barter starter into the gold pan, then threw in (for free), some directions on how to get to the Gallatin River (via Wickiup Creek), and the relative civilization of Virginia City. And that's when the chief's wife started telling them about all the pretty yellow rocks (or stones), found upstream there.

This, of course, signaled Cook, a camas chip frozen in mid-bite, to empty the current contents of the gold pan back into the previous container (a shellacked sheep stomach), and substitute a spyglass in the pan's place. It seems Folsom, Cook and the disillusioned Peterson now couldn't wait to finish their journey (via Wickiup Creek), and rendezvous with the "geologists" of Virginia City, eventually laying claim to being the first expedition to share the wonders of Yellowstone with modern scientific assayers.

The above entry, of course, is by no means complete. There are rumors of other letters having been written—some between great, great, great uncle Willie and great, great, great uncle Oscar in Alaska. That Willie made it up to Canada is pretty certain (who knew if another civil war might break out); that he got all the way up to Alaska for the 1898 gold rush, not so certain. And then there are the Sheepeater legends told around wickiup firewalls and passed from generation to generation, legends of sheep-dipped agents provocateurs (trading in spy wares), and having at one time infiltrated their pacifist meetings. Sounds like a real witch-hunt to me.

But it would all have to be researched nonetheless, with site searches and Wicca hunts—for such things as downloadable Ouija boards (authentic Ojibwa Ouija boards), and solitarot decks. These "research tools" if used correctly, may even be the key to answering other, more pointed questions, questions that I've posed to my immediate relatives—with no direct answers mind you—about cultural confusion, cowardly traits running in the family, and last but not least, who exactly was in charge of middle-naming. And I should be able to do all this just as soon I get back from Software City.

T'wrist & Shout

I had a bad case of the blurs—those low-down, dirty, "how-can-anyone-just-forget-to-focus," blurs. And it's not like the bear cubs cared, hyperactively moving up and down the tree trunk like that. But why should they? Why should anyone? Alas, maybe the "suggestion" scribbled (by Norman), on the photo mailer was right. Maybe I *shouldn't* quit my day job.

And did I ever hate my day job. Okay, so I worked in an *actual wonderland*, one where one could "in theory" step outside on break and snap a National Geographic cover shot. One where one could "in theory" discover a cute coworker, and turn her into a glamorous cover girl. And one where one could "in theory" *paraphrase* the "Dumpster Chicken" (with or without air quotes)—*and* live to tell about it.

But none of that would keep me from occasionally getting down on myself. Because "in practice" I was a cook.

That's right, I said it—a cook. And there's nothing wrong with that, of course—if it's your calling. But if you have other aspirations, say, for instance, to become a photographer/author . . .

"Who's that tap tap tapping at my dorm room door?" I wondered as a half-opened eye found the alarm clock readout. It said 4:45 am.

And it was only Edgar doing the tapping, as usual.

Edgar was one of the 50 some-odd seasonal Park employees I fed, of which 10 or so were indeed truly odd, getting up earlier than me—for no . . . good . . . reason. And they waited . . . waited . . . waited on the porch for me every . . . single . . . morning. But sometimes they couldn't wait. Hence the tapping.

And I swore every summer, that *that* season would be my last—as a cook.

"Nevermore," I cawed, scattering "dumpster chickens" (and a few "porch monkeys"), on my daily dorm-to-kitchen trudge. I fumbled through my keys. Why didn't they just *sleep* a little longer if they needed coffee so badly?

So no, not *all* the summer employees there were cute college-aged would-be models. Some were these semi-retired (odd), couples who seemingly lived, as I liked to complain, for their next meal. They came from all over the country too, each with his or her regional food-favorites, the southerners being the worst. But the hard-core Minnesota Swedes came in a very close second.

And I gagged just a little each time I rolled one of the Minnesotan's so-called "Wrap-scallions"—which were smelt, onions, and kidney beans wrapped and simmered in seaweed. Also called Sar*gasso* (for obvious reasons), this dish wasn't exactly the consensus choice. So I didn't have to roll many. The majority ate my generic baked-codfish-and-au gratin-potato meal, which I happened to have been preparing that very day, that very morning actually, while everyone was still eating my breakfast.

Bleary eyed, I stood at the cutting board mincing onions for the tartar sauce. And like most people, I'd tear up just a little each time I did this, more so if I happened to look up through the window at yet another photogenic, if slightly out-of-focus, day breaking—the blurs seemed to be a theme that summer. Then one of the southerners, Buck, came into the kitchen to "chat."

"Cod? How's come you never fix catfish?"

So I grudgingly wrote *catfish* on my ever-expanding order list and went back to mincing. But Buck, for whatever reason, then felt obliged to comment on my chopping technique, speculating on whether or not I pranced like I minced.

And they all *loved* to comment—almost as much as they loved to eat. And one comment always led to another, this one leading to a remark about my "namby-pamby" stainless steel chef's knife, which was a not-so-subtle way, I think, of bringing up his hobby—knife-making.

"Did I ever show you my Bowies?" Buck asked.

"Your buoys should stay in their neighborhood bro," I answered, mixing and pureeing my pop culture references. And apparently this statement was his cue, to "fetch" the knives anyway—and *Amber's* signal to enter.

Amber was my token dishwasher that summer. Dressed in sweats, and probably hung-over, she did her sleepy but flirtatious little "I know I'm late" turn on the kitchen catwalk. I called it her daily purr-Amber-late. And she knew that I could never get mad at her. But when I didn't even pretend-reprimand her, and when we finally made bleary eye contact, she figured something had to be wrong.

"Sorry about the bear cubs," she said, guessing the depression de jour. "They don't realize how famous they could've been. But maybe we can meet somewhere later on tonight and finish those Victoria's Secret shots."

She knew just how to push my shutter buttons (and presumably how to make Norman the mailer-writer's day too). But before I could even brighten a little, or excuse her (so she could go back and "get a few more winks of beauty sleep"), Buck returned.

And I should mention here that as much as I hated my job, I really didn't hate the people I fed. It just seemed that way. They even found me to be somewhat amusing—like a clown. And that *particular* day just happened to feature my Emmett Kelly sad-clown routine—a thoroughly pathetic pantomime.

And the performance of this pantomime began with my cutting Buck off at the open double-doors to the dining room (laypeople weren't allowed in the kitchen). I then feigned interest in his knives—which, by the way, was definitely the hardest part of the whole routine. But the location, there at the double-doors, was also key—mainly because of the witnesses. And out of those many witnesses, I happened to spy Monroe, from Maryland, who promptly saw me too—and his opportunity.

"Hey, why don't we ever have crab cakes?"

He also knew how to push buttons—the wrong ones. You see they all knew I died just a little inside whenever anyone "suggested" something. So to illustrate this "death"—by suicide—I promptly grabbed Buck's biggest Bowie (much like one would a short shiny fiddlestick); located the dull backside of the knife; and proceeded to "play" my upturned Stradivarius wrist—to the tune of, "nevermore." Actually, I think I shouted something like, "neverm . . . *mama!*" which is approximately when I dropped the knife, and snapped my suddenly-free knife-hand over the wrist.

The audience, of course, ate it up. Some of them even chuckled out loud—more so at my *shocked*-clown *expression*, I think, than at the stark-ravin' misquote. And the laughter only increased as the photographer "slash" author cautiously removed his hand—revealing red—and slapped it back over the wrist. Monroe—having stated that he'd "seen that trick" told everyone it was just ketchup—and then started a chant of, "crab cakes . . . crab cakes . . . crab cakes . . ." whereupon Amber made her, "curtain call," (wondering just how anyone could have possibly known her secret pet name). Likewise, how was *I* to have possibly known that the little dip found on the *presumably dull backside* of all authentic bowie knives is instead routinely sharpened—to a razor-like edge.

Later, at the clinic, the on-duty doctor decided to forgo stitches in favor of gluing my wrist shut. He even told me that the medical adhesive they used to do that was nearly identical to Crazy Glue, a remark he instantly regretted. The physician then brought up the delicate subject of counseling and gave me a pamphlet.

I then felt the need to explain the injury, to which he replied,

"An accidental self-inflicted intentional knife wound? In a room full of people?"

Amber, who drove me to the emergency room (in her *amber*lance), and who was there supposedly for moral support, made some sort of condescending facial gesture behind my back, and tried to cover it up with a yawn. Seems she didn't believe me either. But at least it made for a few good "sympathy pictures" later on. And the drive to our trysting spot, Dunraven Pass, was pretty wild—crazy actually— if only because Amber liked to scatter "dumpster chickens" as much as I did. The next morning, however . . .

"Who's that tap tap, tapping at my dorm room door?" It was only Edgar—again. And later, after getting his coffee, and then his breakfast, he wanted to know when we were going to have pan-fried chicken.

"Soon," I cackled between crow's feet. "Actually, we're having 'squab' for dinner tonight."

I then contemplated my wrist. Luckily, no major arteries had been severed, nor any tendons. And although the doctor said I could someday "play the violin" again, he didn't recommend an "audience." And now that I think of it, he also said to take it easy on the "air quotes" for awhile—at least with my left hand. No problem there. In fact, I'd always toyed with the idea of using some sort of substitute prosthesis for that anyway—no matter how fowl. I also took it upon myself to regularly reinforce my wound with "Crazy" Glue, carefully letting it dry before getting down on myself. And that's not as easy as you might think—when plucking "squab."

Now, if only I could get yet another assist from Amber when making Monroe's special angel food crab cake. Heh, heh, heh! Nevermore.

The Few, the Proud, Thwart

"We shouldn't be doing this," I said, squirming in the back-seat. "Watch it Tulip—that tickles!"

"Aren't thunderstorms romantic?" she'd reply.

"It's not a . . ."

Tulip would then normally giggle, but as the car lurched forward, out of the so-called "storm" we found ourselves staring through the window at a large gnarled knot of diseased elm, a smoldering visage in dire need of some sort of procedure—cosmetic tree surgery perhaps—or at least another "flashion makeover." A "flashion make-over" (for those of you non-cosmologists), is a last-ditch procedure almost always performed by Zeus himself (using a special lightning rod applicator). And I say *another one*, because the previous Saint *Elm*o intervention obviously didn't take. The "thing" sported horn-rimmed gradual-tint Foster Grant sunglasses, and an equally-hideous lichen-like soul patch.

And as we sat, transfixed by this horrific image, a hole just above the soul patch opened up revealing a separate ecosystem unto itself. On closer inspection the hole appeared to be a kind of nesting cavity, with a bird—a small woodpecker-like bird—symbiotically processing some sort of discharge—manually—as if for the hearing-impaired. Or it could've just been a mouth and a weird looking tongue. We weren't quite sure—until milliseconds later,

"I'm trying to run a carwash," it growled, periodically waiting for Uvula (the sapsucker suck-up), to catch up.

"How can I possibly do that . . . with you playing Casanova . . . in a customer's *Nova*?"

At this, Uvula (F. Buckley), signed off, using, of course, the appropriate tongue gesture.

"See ya," said a suddenly shrinking Tulip, slipping out the side door.

"Well?" the entity insisted, its beard blanching upward along with the gradual-tint lenses, as if somehow measuring gastrointestinal *imbalances* of ph.

And other than offering up a half-eaten antacid (from the ashtray), as proof of my goodwill, I really didn't have an answer. He had me. Fact is, he had me in several different locations ever since my first punitive position change at Butternut's Bubble Barn—having then gone from, "Rear End Wiper," to, "Intra-posterior-Window Spritzer,"—under vaguely similar circumstances. This time I was to be given one last chance—in the carwash's laundry—otherwise known as the Cruel and Unusual Servitude Section (C.U.S.S. for short). And much like the rate of *towels* washed there, the employee turnover rate, in C.U.S.S., could also be considered high volume—much higher, I might add, than in many of the establishment's so-called glamour departments.

That said, becoming a carwash employee isn't nearly as difficult as one might first think. It's really just a matter of being in the right place at the right time—a convenience convergence—with cosmic forces, of course, playing a key role. Now suppose that these forces—vibrations that influence all our thought processes—just happen to influence yours to the extent that daydreaming about them causes you to make a "wrong" turn onto a carwash conveyor? What would you do then? And what would be your ideal deportment, or deportmentality as I like to call it?

Would you force the issue? Do nothing? Perhaps you'd stop talking so loudly about deportments—as in "of immigration."

My advice—(having lived through this exact situation): do what you will, inasmuch as you *have* no will. It's all just happening.

If that's not an option then just sit back and relax. Let your central nervous system take over. *It* will soon signal your lungs to cease any and all meditative "breathwork" while entering the vortex of brushwork, that is, if you're still *on* your bicycle.

And it's precisely this kind of wholesale acceptance (or someone else's resignation), that'll get you noticed by management; as will steadfastly maintaining the "limp position," during the freestyle portion of said rinse-cycling event. Furthermore, when applied to the conceptual framework of a hand-to-mouth existentialist world-view, it all but proves the theory that there are no meaningless or ordinary events—that everything matters, as does nothing. And although the seemingly random inability to pay for a particular service (like hot wax), does tend to flesh-out an otherwise insufficient resume, nepotism is still preferable.

As such, the aforementioned Tulip just happened to have a little brother who also worked at Butternut's—*little* and *work* being the two loosely translated operative words. And I'd always wondered how, exactly, the twelve-year-old managed to avoid school, it being late November, and every other employee there at least possessing his or her Grade School Equivalency in puberty. But unlike those, highly "compartmentalized" traditional workers, the kid knew the carwash business in its entirety—from soap to chamois—and for what it's worth didn't seem to mind being called: Mole. Maybe it was better than his real name, which, from what I could gather, was Merle. Or maybe it was just a matter of a mispronunciation. Who knows?

But at that time I really didn't care. What did interest me was the knowledge that, ideally, two fully mature adults were meant to man the laundry. I, of course, wound up being paired with the stubby young truant.

And even over-staffed, the carwash laundry would have ranked fairly high on the Universal Scale of Travail. Most experts rated it right below #24: Hybrid Seed-Corn Detasseling. Factor in child labor laws, allowing the average preteen proletarian twenty-seven-minute breaks on the half hour—leaving me to work alone—and it skyrockets to the lofty #3 position, just barely beating out: Being Chained to a Treadmill Siphon-Crank, whereupon one would theoretically slog bilge all day from a leaky Spitzburg tuna clipper.

Lucky for me, I was only indentured. But the fact remains that I worked my fingers down to the proverbial nub, while *his* workday pursuits alternated between channeling Jimmy Hoffa, and honing his vast nougat-consuming skills.

And because of our location next to the blower, the two of us had to wear O.S.H.A. mandated earplugs, which made communication (with or without Uvula), difficult to say the least. So when he actually was there, the little sadist took it upon himself to let's just say, actively explore the many *alternative* methods of self-expression. If, for example, he thought that I had loaded the extractor improperly, an unexpected "nudge" from his cyborgesque "hip" would send me reeling into a pile of towels. Other times he would stomp on my foot before pointing out an error. Likewise, a forearm to the kidneys rarely failed to get my full, undivided attention, and usually signaled his departure for the candy machine.

It was becoming clear, too, that Merle the Mole Boy and I co-existed in this singular space-time continuum, only because grade-school principals were even *less* receptive to head-butts than certain carwash employees. And it reached the point to where I even thought about retaliating. But I didn't, of course—for the following reasons: A) a lifelong penchant for social compliance; B) his sister, and a similar life-longing for her particular brand of social compliance;

and C) the ultimate realization that his father, Burl Butternut, owned the carwash, and not only was he rather non-compliant, he was also the cedar-chested, Tweety-tongued tree trunk who had admonished me for the incident in the backseat with Tulip (then unknown to me), his daughter.

It also became apparent that "Mole" meant company spy. I couldn't so much as *look* in Tulip's direction without him promptly reporting to Papa. Thus, with these and other such observations coalescing in my crucible-like cranium, were the necessary links forged in the following chain of events:

I arrived at work early one morning and found Tulip there to meet me. She presented me with a photograph of herself—a five-by-seven glossy print. Of course I immediately saw "The Informant" approaching, and thinking quickly—or not—shoved the portrait down the front of my work pants, which ordinarily wouldn't have been too uncomfortable were it not for the four-and-a-half pound zink-plated metal frame.

Tulip then withdrew to her section of the building, leaving me and "little brother" to load the washers. Reluctant to remove the excess hardware from my pants with him there, I decided to wait until one of his many breaks. And I would have made it too, had the merry Munchkin miscreant not picked *this* seemingly meaningless moment to deliver one of his famous head-butts to the image of Tulip, which was, of course, still in the crotch portion of my pants—frame and all.

So visualize if you will, a montage of America's Most Painful Home Videos—hosted by Johnny Knoxville. Now visualize me. Even Mole Boy had a momentary look of concern—clearly a first for him. My big moment, however, featured the Charleston, which I performed, in fast-forward mode, for maybe a full three-tenths of a second, before breaking into the Funky Chicken's less dignified disco version of said dance, eventually tangling my feet in a loose cord and falling to the floor on my back.

A look of horror then appeared on Tulip's face as she walked by and saw me lying in a pool of water with my feet in a snarl of wires. And apparently this sight was instrumental enough, in and of itself, to have spawned two separate conclusions—hers and mine. Hers burst into bloom right away. Mine, coming from the above-it-all perspective of an out-of-body experience, and wholly dependent on hers, began to bear fully formed fruit only after months of careful scrotiny (a term I coined), and proposed that possibly the sequence of events occurring next stemmed from her (rather hasty), conclusion that I had just then suffered an electrical shock, and needed immediate Tulip-to-lip resuscitation.

But before I could disengage from and set the record straight with my rescuer "Internal Affairs" had dragged daddy over to witness this emergency saliva transfusion. And if by chance that scene wasn't disturbing enough to him, Tulip made it worse, or so it would seem, by pulling her picture out of my pants like I was some sort of paralyzed Polaroid One-Step.

And although admittedly a somewhat revolting development, not to mention slightly out of focus, it was, nevertheless, an example of what's commonly known (in certain parts of Hell), as a watershed moment. Time actually quivered, before ceasing to exist. And legend has it that the same foggy fugue of confusion continues to linger eerily over the workstation, to this day spooking the occasional stray cat, and some sensitive humans when they pass by.

But amazingly, no hard feelings resulted—even though a main fuse had indeed mysteriously blown, shutting down most of the machinery. Hence, the whole place had become silent—almost tomb-like. And it was at that point, of course, when I fully expected Uvula to fly out and start pecking me directly, or at least to see a noticeable change in the father's biofeedback beard. But all a bemused Burl Butternut could do was stare down at the two of us, more astonished I think than angry. Who knows? Maybe one of the cats got his uvula.

And normally in these situations, I would have mumbled some nonsense about being framed, or the proper procedure for artificial respiration. But this time I simply stood up, shook the residual shards of non-glare glass from my pant leg, and backed slowly into the office to sign my termination papers, which had conveniently remained on the top of the desk since day one.

Later, as I drove away (mangled mountain bike mounted on my car rack), I asked myself how I could have been so addled as to get mixed up with a lame job like that in the first place. All because of a stupid wrong turn. I swore that it would never happen again, as this time I stopped for directions.

"A service station? There's one five blocks south of here," the pedestrian informed me. "You can't miss it—it's right across the street from the Armed Forces Recruiting station."

"Is it full-service?"

"Why yes," he said. "In fact they even salute you before filling your tank."

Retro Petrol—it sounded like my kind of place.

A Park Caller Caldera Error

Somewhere, neither east nor west of the Rockies—but directly astride the Continental Divide—a vehicle sits in the darkness. Its lone occupant stirs and then peers out through the back window at an extremely upset carwash manager. The startled occupant then reacts to this strange sight—and accompanying thunderclap—by turning on the dome light with the top of his skull, perhaps so he could better see the drink he was stirring spill onto the mattress of the van.

But no, another flash of lightning shows the visage to be merely a gnarled knot of diseased pine, a huge relief to the occupant, who really didn't need any more flashbacks at that point in his life (see previous chapters).

Still another flash identifies the occupant to be the author, the same one who likes to ghost-write about himself in the third person, and stir in the back of his van at 3:00 am.

Not only does he like to stir his "Instant Breakfast" (glucose polymer powder stored in one of his two plastic 5-gallon pickle buckets), at odd hours, but sometimes he'll even eat his "Eventual Brunch" (Kellogg's dry cereal stored in the other pickle bucket), right around breakfast time. The bat guano previously stored in the buckets and meant for his parents' garden back home in Nebraska never made it past the East Gate—thanks to ranger Red Smythe. And we'll just leave it at that for now.

The author/occupant then finds a Los Angeles radio station, KFI 640 AM (which is only possible, FYI, at *3:40 in* the morning), and listens while mixing up a new batch of glucose polymer. He adds a teaspoon of wheatgrass granules for flavor before hearing a talk show host's popular refrain:

West of the Rockies—on our special caldera hot line—you're on the air. What's your name and where are you calling from?

Caller: I'm Bill. And I'm calling from a bunker—at an undisclosed location in Southeast Idaho.

Host: And you have something to add to our ongoing Yellowstone supervolcano discussion?

Caller: Um, yes. I've been a potato farmer in this area for most of my life, so I feel it's important to inform you and your listeners that we wouldn't even have the kind of soil needed to grow such great crops here if not for all of Yellowstone having once erupted. They don't call Ashton Idaho *Ash*ton for nothing.

Host: Very interesting. So I take it you'll be living in your root cellar for awhile.

Caller: Bunker. And you better believe it.

Host: Thanks for the call.

The author/occupant (or "authupant" as he'll be called for awhile), downs his "breakfast" in three quick gulps, starts the van's engine, and continues listening.

Host: East of the Rockies—you're on the air.

Caller: Hi. This is Brad. I'm calling from Davenport Iowa and . . . something happened to me last week that I think might be related to the Yellowstone supervolcano.

Host: Go ahead caller.

Caller: Well, you see I'm a bagger at a local supermarket here, and as I was helping this lady and her daughter out to their vehicle with the palette of cereal they'd bought, I . . .

Host: I'm sorry caller, I hate to interrupt, but did you just say you were helping a lady out to her car with a whole palette-load of cereal?

Caller: Yes, Frosted Flakes actually.

Host: Okay, I just wanted to be sure I heard you right. Please continue.

Caller: Well, as I was helping them out to their U-Haul trailer I couldn't help but notice even *more* dry cereal *inside* the trailer—a different type, but the same brand.

Host: My God caller! What do you suppose they planned to do with all that cereal?

Caller: Well, the lady said she and her daughter were collecting the prizes inside the boxes and if they got the specially marked one, as prophesied in the Cabbala, they'd win a chance to live in some sort of Kellogg biosphere, or you know, maybe the one in Anchorage— I'm not real sure.

Host: Maybe she meant Epcot in Orlando.

Caller: Or it might have been the Cabela's in Nebraska, but that's all beside the point, because she later said something that made me doubt her first story. You see, it was after I commented on the daughter's Yellowstone hat, and I should probably say here that everything the two of them were wearing—sweat pants, shirts, caps—*everything* seemed to have either a bear or a geyser or the word Yellowstone on it. Very suspicious. Even their car had Yellowstone bumper stickers plastered all over it, and the words "Old Faithful or Bust" written in soap on the back window . . .

Host: Did you have a point you wanted to make caller?

Caller: Well, that's when—after I commented on the hat and noticed all the other cereal—that the mother may have let something slip. You see, she mentioned that she'd forgotten that her son the ranger didn't like Cocoa Crispies, and that's why she was now buying just Frosted Flakes. She then said that she knew someone else in

Yellowstone on whom she could possibly foist the Cocoa Crispies.

Host: So let me get this straight caller—she actually used the word *foist*?

Caller: . . . while at the same time not ending her sentence with a preposition.

Host: That is interesting. Do you think perhaps she could have been some sort of time traveler, a grammatically-correct mobster-mom from some other era?

Caller: I'm not sure, host. But I think you're missing my point . . . the lady's *son* is a *ranger*, a ranger in Yellowstone National *Caldera*!

Host: Well, there you have it folks. A small cabal of federally-employed rangers are having their moms stockpile food for possible consumption in a secret Alaska or Nebraska biosphere. Proof positive that they know something we don't. And when we come back, we'll talk to ceriologist/seismologist Howard Quisp, author of the new book *How to Prosper in the Wake of the Great Quake*, and we'll see how his predictions of the looming elongation of the earth's crust tie into all the weird happenings in and under Yellowstone Park. But foist—a message from our sponsor.

Weird happenings? This authupant resided in Yellowstone (or the surrounding National Forest if ranger Smythe ever asks), and just couldn't see anything out of the ordinary even if he wanted to. The only major crustal stretching in the Park of which he had any knowledge, occurred via the elastic in his own underwear, and originated not from deep within *Yellowstone's* bowels.

In fact, the authupant felt so strongly about that subject that he was tempted to call the ever-so-vague (and often confused), talk show host to set him straight. His poor cell phone signal at the continental divide, however, prevented him from doing just that.

And so he forgot all about it—for the most part anyway—until the very next year. In fact it was toward the *end* of the Yellowstone *season* that very next year. You see, traditionally the park closes on the day after the first significant snowfall in November. But it was still October—October 30th to be exact, and actually starting to snow.

The days were short, the nights long, and the radio band wide. And as a result, the same talk show host's program had been coming in quite clearly, but this time, a year later, the host was going on and on about a space ship (or ark), named Era (or maybe it was *from* a different era—who knows, he's always so vague). But this ark was supposedly there to pick up deserving Earthlings just prior to the upcoming Yellowstone supervolcano eruption.

Just then a knocking sound was heard on the van's drivers'-side window—causing the authupant this time to turn *off* the dome light with his skull. It apparently also caused a dislodging of some Halloween decorations from the inside of the van's back window.

The authupant, walking on his knees, then made his way to the driver's-side door and answered it—by rolling down the window and congratulating the young man who stood there.

"Great costume! You look almost like a *real* ranger."

The ranger cleared his throat.

"All I have is glucose polymer powder," the authupant continued. "But you're welcome to some of that . . . so long as you don't play any tricks on me."

"I'd just as soon see some I.D."

"It's me," the authupant protested. "You probably didn't recognize me right away through all the ash, er I mean falling snow."

And it was actually starting to snow quite heavily at that point.

"I still need to see your license and registration."

"Just so you know," the authupant then said (in his best Vincent Price Dracula voice), before handing the officer some I.D., "I wasn't sleeping. I was just in the laboratory." (He only called the back of his van 'the laboratory' on Halloween). "I was listening to the radio and filling unused straw wrappers with, uh . . . pixie dust."

"Is that all?" ranger Smythe said in his best *sarcastic* Vincent Price voice.

"And then, of course, I was going to drive on down to the National Forest to *legally* spend the night."

The ranger handed him back his I.D.s.

"Sure you were. But before you take off, seeing as how we're such good buddies and all, you probably wouldn't mind turning back on your 'laboratory's' dome light, so I can better see what's back there?"

"Uh, no. I wouldn't mind . . ." the authupant/suspect said, ". . . but are you really sure you want to see 'the hamper' (which is what the authupant/*suspect*, or authupuspect, called the back of his van every other night of the year), it's a crusty mess," which the authupant/suspect is sure now—long after the fact—sounded (through his Vincent Price lisp), as if he said, "crusty *meth*," which he's sure in turn sounded enough like "*crystal* meth" to warrant further investigation.

And it's at this point that this author (the same one who likes to write about himself *writing about himself* in the third person), feels almost compelled to state that as someone who's never intentionally possessed or ingested an illegal substance in his life, this author had been suspected of doing just that to a greater degree and with a wider variety than anyone in the annals of modern-day prohibition. It's understandable, though, given how weird he is. But it's also this innocence of his that explains why he never minds complying with authoritarian wishes.

So as the light came on, and ranger Smythe shuddered at the ghastly sight, his well trained eye then fell upon a small patch of green—Kelly green plastic—half buried under the clutter of clothes. He then recognized the plastic as being a part of one of the two most infamous pickle buckets ever to be buried in the back of a mobile home hamper/laboratory. The lid was already off but the bucket was way in the back, on the drivers' side, so phase two of the investigation was in order. Phase two involved going outside in the freezing cold and opening the van's hatchback.

And there they stood, at the back of the van amid all the white stuff flying through the air—at an open tailgate.

"You don't mind, do you?" a smirking Smythe then said, dipping a licked finger into the bucket and sampling some of the "Instant Breakfast," which, of course, instantly passed inspection, maybe even with flying colors. And I only say *flying colors* because being *blueberry* flavored glucose polymer—it (in combination with the frigid temperatures), instantly turned the officer's tongue and lips a rather deep shade of cobalt. And as Smythe's smirk morphed into this sort of "smurph," he noticed the other already-opened pickle bucket, on the opposite side of the van.

"Still illegally collecting bat guano I see," he said. "And I suppose it's for your parents' garden again, huh?"

He then squeamishly reached in and picked an odd-shaped object from out of the bucket. "You could have at least removed the bats?"

Perplexed, the authupuspect, forgot for a moment about all the psychedelic mushroom-growing insinuations of the past, pondered the similarities between cocoa-flavored breakfast cereal and "mushroom soil," and then recalled the Halloween decorations that had at one time been attached to his van's inside-back-window. And he was about to explain everything. But ranger Smythe persisted,

"Okay, where'd it come from? I know it wasn't from Lake Hotel this time. They cleaned up their little bat problem years ago."

"Actually, I got it from ranger Johnson," the authupuspect said. "But it originally came from his mom. She brought in a large shipment last year when she visited him. He didn't like it, so as usual I got all his overstock."

And as so often happens around ranger Smythe, the authupuspect then suddenly got "the munchies" and squeam*less*ly reached into the bucket, cupping a large handful of the brown substance.

You probably can guess what happens next—all further interrogation ceases while chewing (of Cocoa Crispies) commences; the ranger gives up and walks back to his cruiser, the smirk morphing back into its original shape (through which, by the way, he mumbles something about open container laws); and the resurgent author/occupant/*former* suspect simply stands there, crunching away, and contemplates getting a large open container of powdered *milk* for next season.

And as he later slid on down the snowy east slope of the Rockies toward the National Forest campsite, he once again couldn't help but consider calling the radio talk-show host. His mind was a little more open now though. Maybe the talk show host and his guests weren't the cranks he suspected them to be. And so maybe, just maybe the ark called Era did exist, and had a seat reserved just for him. Naw, on second thought, it was meant for *deserving* Earthlings. And this ghostwriter wanted to go down with the ship.

The Joy of Running Amok Luck Club
(or Das Boot)

The question has come up lately as to whether or not Hitler's Brownshirts weren't really just a bunch of schmocks. I, for one, say they were. Because what is a "schmock" anyway? You add some sleeves to the Führer's art smock; toss it and some mock muck (or burnt sienna), into a washing machine—and presto, you got yourself a schmock, and possibly a movement.

You need to be careful, though, never to confuse the schmock with the schmuck (the sleeved kind especially), as I once did. And being a schmuck myself—an easily confused one (with quasi-Aryan bad looks), who's traveled throughout the land of Giardia (and vice-versa), I know mock muck. I know *real* muck too. In fact, I set the trend (a movement itself, of sorts), for the wearing of sharts, long-sleeved sharts at that.

Like the time the whole schmock question came up. It was at my discussion group. Why anyone would want to discuss just *me* is what really should have been discussed, and totally mystifying. But it was flattering nonetheless. And while I modestly tried to steer the subject to other matters, the large scary man who held my hand—or rather my left pinkie finger, insisted on getting back to *me*. But I can be insistent as well.

"Is that a T-shirt you're wearing *over* your *long*-sleeved shirt?" I asked.

He released his grip slightly. "Uh, yeah."

"Why?"

"What do you mean *why*?"

"I mean—does that particular layering order serve some sort of purpose, or did you base-jump into the Cumberland Gap?"

"A lot of people I see are doing it," he ambiguously countered, the pinkie-hold tightening back up.

"A lot of people are wearing schmucks?" I asked back, deciding to name the style right then and there. "If a lot of people wore shorts over their long pants would you do that too?"

He looked over at the Grand Imperial High Falutin who nodded, which was the signal to kick it up a knuckle—the popping sound of which could be heard in Cracow.

They no-doubt must have thought that I was referring to "all those people" he saw *as* schmucks, or worse—going back to the whole *schmock* topic. Stupid fashion Nazis. They're why (in case you ever start a discussion group about me), I can never "pull off" wearing a pinkie ring—on my left hand anyway.

And there're a lot of things that I can't pull off (or put on), besides pinkie rings. It's probably why, out of protest, I started the very first Muklukclub.

And, as I'm known to non-sequitur from time to time: You have to go *somewhere* to work for the winter. Why *not* West Yellowstone—again? As familiar and hum drum as that little border town was to me, it was still infinitely better than the northern Idaho ski set I'd just left, with their elitist—or as they themselves even called it "supremacist"—White Powder group. But just because you don't meet the pompous standards of a ski resort clique (or pass their drug test and/or drugs), doesn't mean that you can't be in the over-the-snow travel business—snowmobiles that is, or as we called them for short: snowmos.

And along about November of each year the snow would indeed fall, and the snow *mofos* (as *I* called them), from Wisconsin, Minnesota, and the Dakotas would begin to migrate west, a bunch of towheads towing their "sleds" behind four-wheel-drives. Day and night, to and from the national park and the bars, the snowmo*motors* never really ever shut down. One or a thousand was always operating somewhere—until the spring thaw. You eventually got used to the constant roar of these motors. And you eventually got used to the reckless driving on and off the streets. But the one thing you never really ever got used to in the West Yellowstone winter season—was the cold. At least I didn't.

On any given day the weather channel could feature this town as the coldest spot in the continental U.S. And one winter that I lived there it set the record for continuous snowfall. So *bundling-up* wasn't just the West Yellowstone soft drink of choice, it was a way of life.

And as a chaser, most residents drank the Gore-Tex brand Kool-Aid. Gore-Tex® snow pants, Gore-Tex® coats, Gore-Tex® gloves, Cerebral Gore-Tex® hoods (minus the eyeholes that I'd encountered in Idaho), and of course—Gore-Tex® boots. But such fabric (even though it was "invented" by a Democratic non-Fascist former vice-president turned global-warming proponent), is expensive. And so why take the chance of ruining it at work—hence the mukluk.

The cheap three-dollar thrift store mukluk—perfect for mucking toilets and long sprints through the SnoMoMotel's courtyard, where, it just so happens I decided to work that winter. And as "lead mucker" at the SnoMoMotel, I had almost every room-attendant working there high-stepping around in these French *non*-designer Jacques boots.

As their leader, I also suggested we add cheap black ski-masks and traditional long underwear to our ensemble. Our motto: who cares if the cuffs don't match the collar? Needless to say, we didn't have a lot of rules in the Muklukclub. A short-sleeved shirt *over* a *long*-sleeved one, however, was the one item totally verboten.

But no one would have seen it anyway what with a parka necessarily covering everything—covering everything at least until the assigned room attendant *entered* the overheated room to be cleaned. Then a quick strip-down would begin, starting with the winter outerwear and followed by the bedding.

And the overheated room assigned to this room attendant, the one standing out beyond all others in his mind from that winter, the one rented for the entire week by what thankfully turned out to have been a very forgiving newlywed couple from Fargo, North Dakota, the one on whose door this same room attendant repeatedly knocked before entering, and the one whose shower still ran, drowning out said loud knocks—*its* strip-downs were somewhat abbreviated that one fine day. And it set up the following case of mistaken identity:

"Where'd you get those stupid looking boots," the occupant of the motel room would giggle as she exited the bathroom, her towel going from drying her lean taut body to becoming a turban in two or three quick motions. These motions, of course, are only assumed since they occurred at about the same time said room attendant (me), reached up to pull off his face mask in a sort of reverse-turban move, which—allowing for the six-inch-long necks on such garments— (and when executed to imperfection), sometimes takes about two or three motions in itself to fully clear the wearer's eyes.

Luckily, as it turns out, the husband would be fairly understanding with regard to such laws of elasto-kinesthiology. It was, after all, the same style of long-necked mask that he—at that point on his way back from a coffee-run to the SnoMoMotel office—had presumably bought at a downtown Fargo thrift store. We had similar tastes in parkas too.

And looking back (which, by the way, isn't easy to do through concussive sound waves), I realized (probably while passing the same threshold over which the husband had earlier carried his bride, and despite the visual/aural distortions—in "slowmo" no less), that the couple could easily have been honorary members of the Muklukclub had circumstances only been slightly different—her distorted cuffs not matching her distorted "blond" collar.

But "The Scream" (as it's been called in Belgrade by earwitnesses), also caused a somewhat less-ironic—nearly-impossible-to-get-out—brown stain or two, most likely from the Java juice. (You'd think Fargoans could hold their coffee a little better). And the housekeeping manager, who assumed that I was galloping through the courtyard to escape facing some sort of responsibility or another, really didn't know *this* over-the-snow mofo's gastrointestinal tract-record.

Apparently he also hadn't read the tract that informed a person of the insidious parasite known as giardia, which, according to the brochure, can sometimes lie dormant for years until awakened by some unusual event or another—for example, a loud screeching noise coming from a naked lady in a motel room. For what it's worth, the motel manager also thought a "*parasite*" designed mukluk fashions.

This same manager also didn't know that some of the employees (okay, just me), had previously dug strategically located privies in the deep adjacent national park snow, for just such gastrointestinal emergencies.

And no, I wasn't running from an enraged husband either, as the other employees would forever recount it. Although I could see why they'd think that, and why some thought I'd gone berserk. After all, Robert Maid Service, the West Yellowstone poet laureate, *had* written all about such horrors.

But no, mine was of a different nature, a microorganistic call of the wild, so to speak, but one to be contemplated and immortalized just the same. And the abbreviated graffitus on the "privy" wall reflected just that:

> There I darted, broken hearted,
> Ruined my pants . . .

83

The ending, needless to say, would have utilized the word *sharted* (had I sufficient yellow ink reserves to finish the job).

And as I sat there, melting, and contemplating making my own "homemade" snow pants (out of real snow), I also thought about where I'd go to work for the rest of the winter. I sure couldn't show my face in West Yellowstone again—until next year anyway. And I couldn't go back up north to Idaho—*it* was becoming too much like Washington, D.C.

And I briefly thought about going back home and working for my uncle Morty in the garment industry, but no, that sounded way too much like a career. Korwin Springs wasn't far away I thought. Then Vegas popped into my mind. Naw, too many pinkie rings.

Real Piggies Don't Go To Market

If you give a thousand pigs a thousand pens one of them will eventually come up with an anti-Stalinist book idea before giving the idea to a thousand monkeys (with typewriters), who'll turn it into something that doesn't even remotely resemble George Orwell's *Animal Farm*, let alone *1984*.

And as a tourist in China I preferred my own pen as well, or maybe to share a pen with one particular person. But that person, the reason I went to China in the first place—well, she pushed the hostel idea on me—*youth* hostels—places that at best slept four to a room. At the worst they slept about ten.

I kept insisting that I didn't feel comfortable in that kind of communal setting. She kept insisting, "When in Rome . . ." and feigned frustration whenever I reminded her of where exactly we were at the time.

"That looks like a nice hotel," I'd say roughly every 15 seconds as we walked the streets of Suzhou.

"That looks like a nice *restaurant*," the girl, Xiaofan, would counter every *other* 15 seconds. The pronunciation of Xiaofan (Chow Fan), by the way, was appropriate because she was in fact, a very big fan of the chow.

But *I* was the one born in the year of the pig. And *I'd* just been on a long, cramped bus ride from Shanghai to Suzhou, taking ironic (if not iconic), snapshots of the traffic in which we were often stuck, traffic that was comprised mostly of livestock trucks, livestock that was comprised wholly of hog—or so it seemed. The hogs, incidentally, would all stare back at me with their beady but empathetic little eyes. And after finally getting off the bus and reuniting with Xiaofan, I couldn't help but notice how *she* was starting to look just a tad bit porcine herself. Sure, it *was* kinda' like the sweet & sour pork calling the chop soooeeeeey "pig," but hey, it is what it is.

To be fair, though, the city of Suzhou has the much deserved reputation of producing some of the most beautiful women in China. And Xiaofan Tan, who was born in that city, wasn't exactly chopped organ meat. She fit right in—even if she didn't still fit right into the size six Levis I'd helped her pick out during our time together in Montana.

"Do you know what I missed most about China when I was in the United States," she asked, without really wanting an answer? "Going to the market every day."

"Was it a Piggly Wiggly?" I asked back just as rhetorically.

"No, it was a tradition," she continued. "You see, back in the olden times we didn't have refrigeration, and so my ancestors had to shop at the market every day for food. Now we just shop every day out of habit and custom. What do you miss the most about the U.S.?"

"I mostly miss staying home," I told her. "Hey, that looks like a nice hotel over there."

"Hey, there's my favorite restaurant over there," she'd then say, breaking the fifteen second rule by about fourteen seconds.

"Where?"

"Over there. Do you see where that guy is making wee-wee into the canal?"

"Which *guy*?" I asked.

"The one with the apron," Xiaofan said. "His name is Vincent—he's their head chef. He makes probably the best head in the China. The best pig head—it's so yummy."

"Pig head?" I said, making no attempt to hide my revulsion! "Isn't there a place anywhere around here where we can have a nice piece of roast beef—a shoulder cut maybe?"

You see, it's always been my policy to not eat any face that used to have a body.

"Come on. You'll love it," she insisted.

But that was approximately one block, seven knockoff Rolex salesmen, twelve roasted sweet potato vendors, six non-Piggly Wiggly markets, five Wii video-game salesmen, three candied fruit-on-a-stick stands, and one sixty-pound undoubtedly very hungry beggar away from our current position. It could take us hours to get to her favorite restaurant—with any kind of luck anyway. And our frequent conversations would only help my cause. Seems some of us can't talk and chew—and walk—at the same time.

"Don't you feel even slightly bad stuffing glazed strawberries in your mouth when this little guy here has none," Xiaofan then asked (in keeping with our long tradition of rhetorical questions)? And the answer, of course, was an unspoken (mainly because I don't talk with my mouth full)—"yes." So we gave what we could to the beggar before going on our merry way.

"You know, you could give that guy even more if you stayed in an inexpensive hostel," Xiaofan said as an afterthought.

"That looks like a nice hotel over there," I said. "What say you and I go up there and I'll teach you a really fun game called This Little Piggy."

"Hey, I think I know that game," she said. And then, after a brief pause, "It's a video game, right?"

"No . . . at least I don't think so," I replied. "It has more to do with my foot fetish than anything else. And since you guys always take your shoes off at the door *anyway* . . ."

"Oh, I get it," she said. And then, after another brief pause, "You men are all pigs!"

I, of course, resembled that remark. Nay, I was the spitting image of it, but protested nevertheless—and at the same time inadvertently dated myself,

"It's really not like that. I swear. I was just *born* in the year of the pig."

At this she calmed down, and a smile even began to form on her all-too youthful, born-in-the-year-of-the-*rat* lips,

"You were? So was my dad. And you know what? Now that I think about it, I know the perfect way to accommodate you."

And it didn't take very long either. It was only one block, three foot reflexology clinics, two Wii video-game salesmen (who knew Wii really did have a "This Little Piggy" game?), and one *elder* hostel registration desk before we reached the bus station's ticket window, where Xiaofan bought me a return trip ticket to the Shanghai airport.

And later that night, after having dined on roasted pig's head—and some swell swill-wine (or s'wine, if you will)—she even gave me instructions on how exactly to *play* the video-game she'd convinced me to buy—the "This Little Piggy" single-player bathroom version of the video-game. And as it just so happens, *Wee-Wee* Wii can indeed be played all the way home.

The Snake Does All the Lines

For those of you who are chronologically-impaired (i.e. young), I should probably explain the title of this story. But I won't. Come on, would Jean Kerr, the popular 1970s humorist extraordinaire, feel the need to explain *her* titles: Please Don't Eat the Daisies, and: The Snake Has All the Lines? No. Titles are only supposed to pique your interest anyway—they don't have to actually make sense. If it gets you reading the first paragraph, it's done its job.

The more important question, though—the one for my lawyer—is: did the snake in *Jean's* book ever slither through *her* car's armrests in search of substance-abusing rodents dashing about in the dash? Because if it did, I'm in big trouble (with the copyright people), and will hereafter resolve to more thoroughly research the literature that I attempt to parody.

And for those of you who made it through the first couple of paragraphs, congratulations to *me*—my mind control efforts have finally paid off. You are now hooked. And you are probably not getting sleepy or anything like that. You're probably wondering if the local narcotics squad knew about all my drug-sniffing helper animals. That's right, I admit to harboring a ménage à rie. But Manny, the ground squirrel living in my dashboard—my little helper who would warn me of upcoming road hazards—*he*, was addicted to *carbohydrate*. It was the *snake* that did all the lines.

And maybe there *are* squirrels on cocaine, maybe they're all around us and we just can't see them, vibrating faster than the speed of light. Manny just wasn't one of them. Me either. But I once suspected a roommate of mine to be using the stuff—more than one roommate actually.

Because, like it or not, there is the occasional hardened criminal "on the lamb" in Wyoming. He might even end up in Yellowstone, detoxing off his bestiality habit through some sort of statewide rehab program. Most of them, however, are just on the horse, or the crack, or the *lam* (from authorities), and aren't trying to detox off anything. And what better place to run from outstanding warrants than Yellowstone National Park, specifically the dorm room of yours truly? Yours cluelessly, though, learned of his roommate's outlaw status well after the fact.

In my defense, the tight-lipped suspect-in-question fled so suddenly—in the middle of the night—out of the second story window—that I didn't have much of a chance to really get to know him. So I also didn't have too many qualms about confiscating the would-be forfeited assets he left behind—four pairs of pants (those four feited me nicely), two shirts, and a shaving kit. All of these items, I reasoned, would have been wasted on the graft-happy law-enforcement rangers anyway, and probably didn't have any forensic value.

Thankfully, such incidents are the exception in Yellowstone and not the rule—like they are at the Grand Canyon. But you have to go somewhere when the summer season ends in Yellowstone. And a place called Victim Hall is where the Grand Canyon human resource people housed transient workers like me. Actually, the place was *named*, "*Victor* Hall," but I soon learned that everyone who lived there routinely substituted the word *Victim* for *Victor*.

And as I checked in with the dorm supervisor there I asked him why. He just pointed to some maintenance men who were in the process of replacing a section of bloodstained Victim hallway carpet. Funny how they didn't mention mayhem in orientation—or depression. Because I'd also heard the rumors that someone had hung himself in the closet of room number 13, hung himself with a coat hanger—a coat hanger that had been neatly knotted into a noose. That room had subsequently been renamed the aeronautical-sounding: Hanger 13.

So naturally, I started plotting *my* flight *out of there* from the moment the knob on room 13's door hit me on my way *in*.

And for those of you who are "chronologically-gifted," or just fond of classic rock & roll, you might be familiar with a little band called Lynyrd Skynyrd. You might even know some of their lyrics. And like most resort bums of that era, I owned a couple of their tapes—one of them: "Pronounced Leh-Nerd Skin-Nerd." I owned a bootleg Eagles tape too, and, of course, a portable device in which to play them. It was the next generation of device—next up from the reel-to-reel type—but it had "Bass-Boost" and a built-in microphone, which for some reason made my *new* roommate at the Grand Canyon somewhat nervous.

Also fairly tight-lipped (at first anyway), this roommate, managed to unpurse his lips long enough to ask me why those two tapes were all the music I moved in from my car.

"Because that's all I have," I explained. "Dashboard Manny ate all my Weird Al Yankovic tapes."

"Thank God for Manny," the roommate then said before offering me full access to *his* tape collection.

"Thanks, but I can't get enough of Skynyrd—especially this song," I said, referring to the one currently playing. "By the way, what *is* that smell?"

"Oh, that's the mule corral," he answered. "And if you like that, just wait 'til the wind blows *this* way."

He then paused from scratching his arm for a second in order to scratch his head and asked, "You call your car's sound system, 'Tape Deck Manny?'"

Manny, my freeloading dashboarder, you see, was always hungry. It's like he had a tapeworm when it came to eating my music. And I think he liked listening to FM radio better than tapes, mainly because he could find almost any song at seemingly just the right moment—from behind the radio—"eating" any *tape* he didn't like. It was uncanny. But I didn't have time to fully explain to my new roommate the phenomenon that *was* Manny; I had to unload the rest of my stuff, which included four pairs of pants, two shirts, and a shaving kit.

My new roommate's shaving kit, by the way, looked *exactly* like my recently appropriated one, and I do mean exactly, except that the *insides* of *his*—as per my accidental examination of it—contained a rubber hose, a bent spoon, and a black sticky substance wrapped in foil.

And the alarmed expression on my new roommate's face said all he wouldn't say, as the accidental examination of *my* shaving kit *by him* took place—the contents of which included, among other things, a toothbrush, and an unbent fork. It's also when he got all nervous again.

And for those of you who are, "literarily-refined," but still hooked, "jonesing" for less exposition and more plot—I'm sorry. You might have to grow your own. Because the rest of my stay in Hanger 13, from that crucial moment on, met merely with appeasing my momentarily enraged roommate—(thus getting the fork off my throat); being (further), grilled by the civil war buff (did you know there was one occurring, as we spoke, in Nicaragua?); and just surviving the first week.

Typically "all over the place," as roommate junkie tweekers often are, this roommate, however, possessed at least a semblance of rational thought—even chuckling a little at the mix-up of personal effects. He then warmed up even further after I assured him that while I *did* sometimes write in bed, under the covers, I wasn't an undercover journalist—even going so far as to show him my writings. Despite all this, the guy still took an unusual interest in my ink pen of all things, which, incidentally, was among the other items found (in the *liner*) of my shaving kit.

"Speedball?" he asked, almost as if offering something.

"No," I answered, "just a really fancy felt-tip or fountain pen. But the ink in it's gone bad—it's all gummed up or something."

The clincher, however, came when I offered to add to his rock collection.

"I couldn't help notice," I said as he went back to some sort of scraping, "that those stones you're working on look a lot like the stones I found in my ex-roommate's shirt pocket in Yellowstone. He sort of gave them to me. The shirts that is."

My roommate then chuckled for the second time that day before commenting, "You're all right. No one could possibly fake that degree of stupidity—or such bad writing for that matter."

And this roommate didn't escape out the window that night—which would have been nice. If he did, though, he probably would have landed (conveniently), on one of the many pack mules below. And he wasn't paranoid like my last bunkmate either. It's almost as if he felt protected (from whatever)—in a park where everything is considered a federal offense. It was kind of strange now that I think back on it.

Opening up even more, he told me he came to the Grand Canyon to escape the smog and fast pace of Los Angeles—which is, for those of you who are geographically-handicapped, just down the road aways from the Grand Canyon. L.A., incidentally, is where, in addition to his lips, he learned to purse his nostrils. And I still don't know exactly what relevance that factoid had, but here, at the Grand Canyon, he said he could *dis*purse with immunity—or something like that. And he spoke of other matters, such as pipes disguised as everyday objects, and various new, more-cost-effective methods of delivery. The man was nothing if not cutting edge.

And we both knew I wasn't really stupid—just really naive. I knew basically what was going on, I just didn't know, nor did I want to know at the time, all the sordid details. But people like my roommate, who was obviously up to his ulna in extra-legal activities, tended to trust me for some reason (they could probably tell I was too timid to be a narc), and usually ended up liking me—even caring to some degree.

"What's the matter?" he once asked. "I noticed you're only playing the *sad* Lynyrd Skynyrd song over and over . . . and over."

"I don't know—I guess I'm just a little depressed. I'm not really liking it here. And I kind of miss my girlfriend Tuesday. But the worst thing is I don't even have the gas money to leave yet."

"I might be able to help you out with that," he offered, "if you're ever headed L.A. way."

I said I'd let him know.

Then it happened—Hell Night that is. Hell Night is something that occurs once, okay sometimes *twice* a night in Victim Hall—seven days a week. But it was already having a cumulative effect on my delicate psyche. And in order to set the Hell Night scene for someone who's never experienced it (or at least the Victim Hall version of Hell Night), one need only to first imagine a crop dusting plane, from Mexico, abruptly discharging its cargo of chemicals and people (people in the form of partying paratroopers), *while still in the hanger*—Hanger 13 in this case.

And me without my flight goggles.

Most of the white powder, I'm guessing, though, came from the fire suppression system inadvertently activated by a mixture of mule methane and smoke—every kind of smoke imaginable.

Still, none of it was my idea of fun. So after finally having had enough, I made my way through the blizzard of sprinkler-system soda ash (and other stuff), stumbling over various passed-out people along the way, and left the "Animal House," to get into my car (the animal house), where I could be more or less alone—maybe even get some much needed shut-eye.

And the next morning I went to see about changing my living situation.

"Oh, Sure. Yeah, I can probably find you a more low-key roommate," the dorm supervisor said, still groggy from his own participation in the previous night's Hanger 13 party. "The guy I have in mind, though, is kind of weird—a hobbyist. But he's quiet."

As long as his hobby wasn't stone carving, I thought. Besides, I'd only have to survive for a couple more weeks, when I'd get my first and final paycheck. After that I'd once again be blowin' on down the road, perhaps to visit Tuesday, who took a job at a borax mine in Death Valley National Park—or something like that.

And seems my roommate wasn't offended by my moving out. He'd even checked up on me once in my new place, asking about my future plans and talking of pack mules and such. The guy was obviously still all over the place when it came to conversation. I mean, what the heck's a "*bowl* of black tar" anyway? And what did it have to do with my fancy but ineffective felt-tip.

And for those of you who are "arachno-freaky" or hoping for a "quick fix," of the grammar in this piece, and therefore want to know just what my *newest* roommate did with the larger more hairy tarantulas that he collected, blame my editor, who censored most of what I wrote about it (and then didn't even fix the grammar), but who did allow the following after-the-fact dialog.

"Don't tell me," the Dorm Supervisor said as I again shook him awake. "Let me guess. You slept in your car again last night and want a new roommate?"

My nervous twitch and the constant brushing of imaginary spiders off my back seemed to answer his question adequately. So he got up and focused his bloodshot eyes on a chart.

"Let's see, there's room 27. The guy in there is sort of an aging hipster. But he doesn't party much anymore."

"Does he have any hobbies?"

"Not that I know of."

And one needn't be clinically naive, as I admit to being, to be *unaware* that the phrase, "not that I know of," was, in fact, the ancient Yaqui incantation that—more often than not conjured up the Wile E. Coyote of all spirit guides, the one whose services specialize in guiding people like me into weird situations. Heck, you could be Carlos Castaneda and not know that.

And for someone said to be aging, that one particular hipster roommate, it turns out, had some very agile hips, not to mention feet that were incredibly fleet. His reflexes weren't too bad either, which when all taken together (and the proper motivation thrown for good measure), resulted in his using those ball bearing hips of his to turn on a proverbial swivel.

But it seems he also had a keen eye, since the mere sight of my tongue's lead taste bud caught in the act of protruding past my lips, is what, I'm guessing, triggered his as-yet burned out nervous system to tell his as-yet burned out body to turn—on that same proverbial swivel—and execute, post-haste, the dreaded "One-Armed Flying-Camel-Clutch to the Mouth"-move, on yours truly, dislocating a minor body part or several in the process.

Yours cluelessly only wanted to borrow a stamp to put on his envelope addressed to Tuesday. And I thought the elephant ones looked kinda' cute. It's not like I wouldn't pay him back. But who knew that my newest roommate was just another of those obsessive-compulsive hobbyists—this one a stamp collector, and that the dancing pink elephant "commemoratives" were such a rare and valuable edition—as were the grinning psychedelic teddy bears.

So after picking me up, dusting me off (turns out I would never totally rid myself of white powdery substances), and questioning me thoroughly, old swivel-hips said it was a very good thing that he caught me in time—before I licked the stamps. I, in turn, after hitting the reset button for my tongue (and relocating as many of its dislocated papillae as possible from the floor), told him that I would be taking a trip soon anyway, calling on my first ex-roommate for some of that help he'd promised me.

And just the gas money would have been enough, but my

benefactor said there'd be "more where that came from" once I made the delivery. My instructions, you see, were to meet a businessman by the name of "Off-Ramp Ricky" in the heart of downtown L.A., not far, actually, from the famed La Brea Tar Pits.

But unfortunately, I'd gotten myself a little lost in that asphalt jungle. Hey, had my pen been working properly the directions I wrote down wouldn't have been so smeared.

And nothing else seemed to be working right for me that week either, including my sound system. Sure, I knew it was inevitable that Manny'd eat my Eagles tape too; they were, after all, natural enemies. But Skynyrd's innards, also wound (or unwound), up, *not* as you might imagine, in Manny's insides, but deep within the (un-named), tape deck's. I'd neglected to clean the heads, of course— which made me mad. It was somewhat fitting, though—mainly because the lyric: "I'll be blowin' down the road" just doesn't seem to work when you're stuck in gridlock.

And for those of you who've ever been "L.A.-waylayed" and are, for whatever masochistic reasons still reading this, you'll no-doubt agree that gridlock is more of a time for *FM* radio anyway—airwaves where you can find SigAlerts, and most likely a station *called* "The Breeze."

But I'm fairly certain that's not where Manny found the Jim Stafford song, "Spiders & Snakes" (in which Jim professes his dislike for those very creatures), it was probably Classy Country 98 FM. But hey, I wasn't paying much attention. I was too busy contemplating the past forty-eight hours.

Tuesday, it seems, must have gotten wind of my arrival because she was gone from Death Valley when I got there. Okay, fine—the place reminded me too much of the Grand Canyon anyway. There were images of mules everywhere—twenty-mule teams in fact—hauling borax (still another white powdery substance of which I didn't need any more in my life).

And the pen on which everyone seemed so fixated—which, by the way, I'm now sure was some kind of airbrush (with a gravity-feed ink reservoir on the end)—wasn't going to help me in my journaling pursuits. So I used a pencil now to scribble the heading to my latest, "downtown-L.A.-gridlock" entry:

"If Life is a Bowl of Black Tar Heroin What Am I Doing at the La Brea Tar Pits?"

Under this title, of course, were the continued third-person musings of a mad man, a man mad at the whole world, not just his tape deck. But maybe things would change, he wrote (occasionally brushing an imaginary spider off his back), maybe he'd get enough money from Off-Ramp Ricky to buy a van with a decent tape deck—one in which he could also sleep more comfortably. It would definitely come in handy at his new job—the one he'd hoped to get at Hotel California—or something like that.

My Least Favorite Year
(or Free Willy or A Boy Named Carrie)

Much has been made of my job cooking for the employees of a general store in Yellowstone National Park. After all, I did it for *seventeen consecutive summers* at various Yellowstone locations. Weird right? Even more weird, is that I was a resort-bum "lifer" in Yellowstone who *didn't* drink or otherwise have some sort of checkered past. But looking back, it was a pretty interesting job. The employees I fed came from all over the country—all over the world really—and spanned the entire socioeconomic spectrum.

And I'm not real sure exactly what "socioeconomic spectrum" means, but it looked good in the company's employee recruitment brochure, and I figured if I used it here, it might impress someone like you who's also bluffing his or her way through life.

But as manager of this small kitchen, some of the company's employees-who-spanned-the-entire-socioeconomic-spectrum—by necessity—had to work under me. The year in question—my least favorite one—featured the usual ragtag crew.

There was me, the manager and head chef (or head hog slopper to be more accurate).

There was the retired career Navy mess hall guy as my sous chef.

There was the young idealistic environmentally-conscious Native American—my *Sioux* Chef. (And just so you know, he wasn't really a member of the Sioux tribe, he was really a *Blackfoot* Indian, just off the nearby Blackfoot *reservation*, and, incidentally, one of the two "Jerky Boys" who worked for me that summer).

There was also the hulking ex-con who kind of missed being in "stir." He was my lead dishwasher.

There was the preppy dining room attendant majoring in socio-economic spectroscopic engineering studies at the university of Hawaii—the other "Jerky Boy."

There was the deranged, nerdy, corpulent, arrogant, blunt, nothing-to-lose, sexually-ambiguous guy with no direction in his life and a maniacal laugh used at inappropriate times misfit, who we other misfits characterized as being a rung or two below misfit status number two dining room attendant.

And then there was Amber, of course, my token other dishwasher.

And in the same way that a lot has been made of my job cooking for the employees of a general store in Yellowstone National Park, a lot was also made that year with regard to the age-old question of whether or not we, as sentient beings, have free will. And by a lot, I, of course, mean very little, my immediate family back in Nebraska making a lot of my seventeen-year cooking career in Yellowstone, and *me* making a lot out of the question of free will.

And we must've had way too much time on our hands that summer, probably due to retired-career-Navy-mess-hall-guy, Willie, who could never really ever fully retire, taking charge from day one and doing most of the important work, because I was actually able to occasionally draw my coworkers into a discussion, a discussion concerning whether or not we (as sentient beings), do indeed have free will.

And I'm not exactly sure just what *sentient* means (or why *sure* isn't spelled with an "h"), but *my* contention regarding the subject of free will was and is that everything, and I repeat *everything*, is all just a combination of nurture and nature—nothing else. There are no truly spontaneous acts. We don't *have* a choice—*in anything*.

Why, for instance, would my Native-American Sioux Chef, or rather the *Blackfoot* Indian just off the nearby *Blackfoot* Reservation, suddenly choose, with no good reason, to be more environmentally-conscious, to in effect *reduce his carbon footprint*.

Did I mention he was a *Blackfoot* Indian?

And I know, that's a long way to go for that one particular bad joke—ten full paragraphs serving as the setup. But it's a pretty good bad joke I think. And the point is—I couldn't help it! I *had* to use it. Time is running out. Carbon paper is practically a thing of the past *right now*. And the phrase "carbon footprint" might not even be apart of our vernacular by the time this piece is published, thus rendering the joke *no longer a joke!* Not only that, it was my only good one—ever—and sadly I've written an entire book of supposed humor, which is a joke in and of itself. People, I'm sure, are currently laughing *at* it the way people with shadenfreude gratuitously derive pleasure at those who slip on banana peels.

And I *am* sure exactly what shadenfreude means (*and* why you don't need a deriver's license), but there's a reason I thought I could be a successful humor writer. I was encouraged! It's not my fault. You see, I once told someone that my butt was as smooth as a baby's face and that same person then started laughing hysterically—for about five minutes. The fact that I was tickling her at the time (one of my best "moves"), and that she abruptly stopped laughing upon her discovery of the un-baby-powdered truth, really should have been my first clue that what I said wasn't really all that funny.

But people (and I'm obviously no exception), generally believe what they *want* to believe—like the misconception of their having any control whatsoever over their lives.

"When exactly did *you* first get control?" I asked "Tater" my hulking ex-con dishwasher who was, incidentally, the one person who didn't necessarily disagree with me. "Did you have a *choice* of whether or not to be *conceived*?"

"Of course not," he answered.

"Did you have a choice of what to eat after you were born?"

"Of course not."

"Did you have a choice of which kindergarten to attend."

"Of course not."

"Did you have a choice of whether or not to cut that guy's finger off?"

"He gave me no choice!" Tater finally said ominously.

Turns out the nickname "Tater" was short for *Amputater*.

"You see?" Soo, my preppy dining room attendant majoring in socioeconomic spectroscopic engineering studies at the university of Hawaii chimed in. "Claiming you have no free will can just be a way of not taking responsibility for your actions."

"And a reason for not taking *credit* for the *good* things you've done," I countered. "It evens out."

"Turn that flippin' light back on, you squirt-for-brains Blackfooted son-of-a-biscuit," retired career Navy Mess hall guy who also fake-swore like a sailor yelled! "I'm slicing' your freakin' buffalo meat over here. What—you want me to cut my own finger off?"

"Sorry," Iron-Eyes Irvin, my carbon-footprint-reducing Blackfoot Sioux chef said. "Force of habit."

And Iron-Eyes couldn't help the way *he* was. His father (Iron-Eyes Sr.), was a Hollywood actor, a commercial actor (just off the reservation), whose most famous role was a 1970s anti-littering public service announcement. The emo actor, tired of being typecast, and not wanting to get into gay porn, then returned to the Blackfoot reservation to study Butchcraft and hence become a butcher (a butch one at that), who would eventually father Iron-Eyes Jr.—a result of his own free will—*or* more likely, a result of some sort of biological imperative.

And I'm not real sure exactly what "biological imperative" means, but it sounded good in the vampire movie I saw, and doesn't explain in the least why Iron-Eyes Jr. also couldn't help but participate in the annual just-outside-of-Yellowstone buffalo hunt. It also doesn't explain the forces at work compelling Soo, my preppy dining room attendant majoring in socioeconomic spectroscopic engineering studies, to go with Iron-Eyes Jr. on this so-called "hunt" and observe the slaughter. But it probably had something to do with class credits.

"By observing tatonka," Irony-Eyes Jr. began, "I see that they don't worry about whether or not we as sentient beings have free will. Sometimes, though, tatonka will step across the imaginary line known as the Yellowstone Park boundary—instinctively searching for grass to eat. And then I blast 'em!"

Chief Seattle he wasn't.

And just so you know, to the best of my knowledge (and anyone who's ever read anything that I've ever written knows to take that knowledge with a prescription-grade saltwater enema), only native Americans are allowed to participate in this yearly bison herd reduction effort.

And in this very same way, much like 100 years ago, every single part of the buffalo is still utilized, with the possible exception of the hide and the organs, or, as it turns out, anything else that might not be considered muscle tissue. This made Soo (the preppy college boy majoring in socioeconomic studies and one-half of the "Jerky Boy" coalition), somewhat disillusioned. The Jerky part of him, though, still helped Iron-Eyes Jr. retrieve this raw muscle tissue stored seventy miles away in the West Yellowstone Taxidermist's meat locker—which, they, of course, eventually brought to our kitchen in Yellowstone for convenient and cheap processing.

And I have to say that much has been made of the heavy-duty cast iron Buffalo-Chopper brand "food processor" that I had at my disposal that year, the corporate headquarters of which I think are in Buffalo New York. And when I say "much has been made *of*," I really mean much ham and chicken and egg salad has been made *with* it. Much less had been made of (or with), the Buffalo-*Chipper* brand *meat smoker*—the marketing folks back in Buffalo having failed miserably in their efforts to give their latest product an appealing name. It's not their fault though. The name "Chipper" was just too enticing.

And the fact is, you could actually use any kind of fuel in the smoker—it didn't have to be buffalo chips—it could be hickory *wood* chips for instance. On the other hand, there was no shortage of the former in Yellowstone National Park.

And who knew what reasons were at work compelling Carrie, my deranged, nerdy, corpulent, arrogant, blunt, nothing-to-lose, sexually-ambiguous number two dining room attendant to, in fact, have writing aspirations of his own—to become a horror novelist. But it might have had a little something to do with his father giving him the Steven Kingian first name of Carrie.

Carrie, who exhibited anti-social behavior on an almost minute-by-basis—and who was the only one to have ever shocked Tater—believed in free will. It might have had something to do with his rebelling against his behavioral-psychologist father.

And so I have no choice but to explain here (despite what happened later), that I've never had the desire to hurt anyone. I don't know why anyone would. And it's not like I think I'm a good person or anything. In my own unique way I'm contributing as much as anyone to the decline of decent society. But because in the past I had been so ridiculed and so humiliated about my appearance—to the extent of even structuring my life so as to eventually become a lone-wolf photographer, ideally one who'd have only minimal contact with anyone possessing so much as a working knowledge of insult comedy—*I* didn't want anyone *else* to feel as badly as I had. Maybe it was just my nature—my empathetic-nature—to break the cycle of verbal abuse.

But I also realized that others have had it way worse than me. And their nature (combined with their nurture), may be to otherwise do unto others what others had done unto them—only worse. And as funny looking as *I* am, my deranged, nerdy, corpulent, arrogant, blunt, nothing-to-lose, sexually-ambiguous number two dining room attendant Carrie, was probably worse-looking. But he was of the *otherwise* nature, and so promptly gave me the nickname "Aardvark Boy"—you know, because of the overall configuration of my face. He even made up an entire story, a horror story (to me anyway), about how my *feral* self was discovered by a P.T. Barnam-like figure and how I subsequently escaped the exploitative carnival sideshow circuit to become an exploited resort bum "lifer" in Yellowstone, only to ultimately be killed—by an equally-exploitative and mysterious "poacher" *not*-all-that-coincidentally named Carrie. It was enough to make me think I was back in high school.

"Causality," I therefore made the mistake of saying to Carrie one day as he set one of the dining room tables. "You couldn't possibly make the decision to take a life right now—mine or anyone else's—because of this lack of causality. In other words, you would need a valid "reason" to kill me."

"What do you want Peterson," Carrie shot back, "directions to the nearest ant hill?"

"All I'm saying—you jerk," I calmly replied, "is there were, and currently are, for that matter, an infinite number of 'reasons' combining and converging on your life to make you what you are right now. So relax, you can't help the way you are—which isn't so bad by the way. I see a lot of great qualities. And maybe, just maybe, *realizing this* will even 'cause' you to become a positive influence somewhere down the road."

At this, Carrie, my nerdy, corpulent, arrogant, blunt, nothing-to-lose dining room attendant got kind of quiet, before eventually relating to me (to the best of his recollections anyway), the exact location of the last ant hill he'd seen, before adding,

"Why don't you go back to Africa—I hear they have giant fire ants over there."

"You couldn't help but say that," I then said. "People who don't like loosing arguments always change the subject."

"Listen," Carrie countered, "Sure, I had no choice but to let my parents feed me rock candy—with a sling shot. And I suppose it had some effect on me too. But you're a fool if you think it kept me from making my own decisions."

I then got contemplative as well, and started imagining the series of events, one of which perhaps involving a demented Nazi scientist with a butterfly net at the Argentinean border causing a random butterfly (or the proverbial one), to start flapping it's wings in Brazil, thus setting in motion the causal chain of events leading to what happened next—the much flapping of *gums* in Yellowstone. But I couldn't help it. It was my second of only two good jokes.

"You chose to use that stale old rock candy slingshot joke," I explained to the corpulent Carrie, "for a number of really bad *reasons*. What you should've said—but couldn't (because I thought of it first)—was that your parents actually fed you *cotton* candy . . . with an insulation blower."

I waited. And then waited some more. But the only rim shot came in the form of a Hobart brand meat slicer (or buffalo slicer if you will), and its parts being slammed down at the dish station—by Willie.

"If you ask me, you two are both full of squirt," Willie said. "I'm going on break now. One of you brilliant clucks are going to have to load the Buffalo Chipper with these bloody buffalo slices. One of you other brilliant clucks might want to think about going out and gathering some chips for the Chipper."

And I gather that the reader has already guessed that only one of those various Yellowstone locations at which I worked, had an actual wood chipper in addition to the Buffalo Chipper and Chopper, and thus the basic ingredients and/or inspiration for, if not a horror novel, at least a true-crime cookbook.

And I don't really know exactly what *chip* means, at least the way Willie would have defined it, or just what kind of chips that aforementioned brilliant cluck collected (or why there's only one "o" in proving). But the chip-collection process coincided roughly with the proving of a *point*, by me—to Carrie.

"Okay then," I said, bluffing, "go get the biggest longest butcher knife we have here in the kitchen, and I'll lay down here on this prep table. You shouldn't have any problem *willing* yourself to take that knife and run it through my heart."

"Alright," he said.

And it was the nonchalance with which Carrie, my nerdy, corpulent, arrogant, blunt, nothing-to-lose dining room attendant said the word *alright* that got my would-be heart kabob to beat just a little faster. The moistening of my skin with perspiration happened at about the same time. And I have to confess that these anxiety symptoms persisted, and even increased during the next sixty seconds when I lay prone on the prep table with the point of what amounted to a large dagger resting on my noticeably beating breast bone. It didn't help that highlighting my, at-that-time glistening epidermis, cans of lit Sterno lined the table in a hastily thrown-together attempt at recreating an authentic Blackfoot sacrificial doofus-alter. For that I sarcastically say thank you Iron Eyes Jr.

And when I say sixty seconds, I, of course, realize that in a situation like that, when, a short time into such a ceremony, when you're mentally going through every possible "reason" someone might have for killing a person, and it dawns on you that while there might be a "reason" that someone's crazy, but that "crazy" doesn't need a "reason," or that calling someone's bluff might be reason enough, it's reasonable for you to then think that time is relative and that three or four decades might better describe that same sixty seconds.

"I *could* do it," Carrie then said, finally withdrawing the knife. "I just don't *want* to."

And here's where the phrase "famous last words" could easily have been ascribed to me when I uttered the following,

"Well, then *will* yourself to want to."

(Another one of those brief/interminable interludes ensued as he put the knife back up to my chest).

"I don't want to," came the eventual petulant reply.

"Well then *will* yourself to *want* to want to."

(Another one of those brief/interminable interludes ensued).

"I don't want to."

And here is where Tater, my hulking ex-con lead dishwasher who kind of missed being in "stir" chimed in,

"Care if I take a stab at it," he asked?

Three or four decades turned into centuries before Tater who had jumped directly onto the stainless steel "alter" and was squatting above me holding the butcher knife against my chest was talked down, or at least beginning soften a little—a result of Willie having just come back from his (two-century-long!), break, and using some of his rather vociferous powers of persuasion.

But as that was occurring, a witness just happened to show up, a guest witness not scheduled that day, but showing up anyway—through the kitchen's back door.

And I repeated emphatically, and I repeat *repeated* to this very witness, this very special guest witness who just happened to show up at the back door, that what was "going on" was merely a philosophical experiment of sorts.

But I doubt she understood much of any of it, what with whatever it was that emanated from my vocal chords quavering the way it did.

And I'm not real sure exactly what trichinosis or brucellosis or halitosis or the definition of *is* is, but there was a lot made *later* that day of the grilling of *me*, the manager and head chef (or head hog slopper to be more accurate), the grilling of me by this same witness, this young, no-nonsense, in her first year, ambitious, female *federal health inspector-witness*.

Lost on her also, was my admonition to "not go in there," when referring the walk-in Buffalo-Chipper brand meat smoker/jerky-maker/sometimes home to Carrie, my deranged, nerdy, corpulent, arrogant, blunt, nothing-to-lose, sexually-ambiguous usually-clos-ing-the-door-to-the-smoker-behind-him-and-waiting-for-someone-to-walk-in-on-him-as-he-eerily-smoked-his-meat, number-two din-ing room attendant.

Did I mention it was my least favorite year?

And some things you just can't tell a health inspectress.

"Permission to go AWOL," Willie, the retired career Navy Mess hall guy who was only *sometimes* de facto manager but who was now conveniently sous chef again asked? "I could really use a flippin' pee break."

And of course the actual manager and head chef (or head hog-slopper to be more accurate), granted him that permission. And Willy was, as you might imagine me saying—free to go.

The Sorcerer's Yellow Stone

Once upon a time, not far from the Oxbow Bend of the Snake River and massive Mt. Moran lived the oxymoronically-monikered mountain man, Richard "Beaver Dick" Leigh. (It's true. Look it up). And often visiting that same area today is a highly acclaimed nature photographer going by the name of Moose Peterson (which is also true). Just how any of this relates to sorcery, or Yellowstone, or even the *author* (whose last name is Peterson), is anyone's guess. It's anyone's enigma really—unless, of course, you're one of the chosen few who believe that occult forces were at work in the author (*me*) making a name for *myself*.

And unlike "Beaver Dick" who redundantly took a wife (a Shoshone slave-woman named Jenny), *I've* yet to marry. But like "*Moose*" I'm a nature photographer, albeit a relatively obscure one. Somehow or another, I did manage to get a couple of small photo essays published, and so naturally spend most of my summers using them (and a book I *bought* entitled: *How to Pick Up Women at*

Promotional Book Signing Events)—to pick up women at promotional book signing events.

"That's the first '*Fannie*' I've ever signed," I would unthinkingly think out loud—too loud, it would seem, for any *dignified* book signing event. I'd then "booty-check" Fannie as she walked away.

And, "Yes," I'd sometimes respond to other ladies' comments (about my bio), "I *have* been photographing longer than you've been alive. Anyone have a problem with that?"

And, "No ma'am," went yet another of my many pick-up lines, "I'm *not* related to Moose Peterson. But try to enjoy the book anyway!"

That one almost became my mantra,

"N'ohhmmmmmm, I'm not related to Moose Peterson . . . n'ohhmmma'am. N'ohhmmmmm, I'm not related to Moose Peterson...n'ohmmma'am . . ."

Then Fannie came back, which wasn't totally unexpected. After all, the book (that I *bought*) assured me that I could indeed draw certain suggestible types back to me using only willpower.

"I meant to ask you earlier," she said in broken English as I sat there—the smug shutterbug, "are you . . . would you maybe . . . might you possibly be . . . related to *Moose* Peterson?"

"Uncle Moose," I said, losing the mantra! "I haven't seen him since we discussed the will. He's pretty big in Japan, huh?"

"Very big—like moose."

She then asked me if I'd give her some photography lessons. It was her first time in Yellowstone—first time in America actually.

So after meeting the next morning at the designated trailhead, we set off walking—me with my 40 pounds of camera gear, her with her Fuji disposable.

And as we hiked, I tried imparting to her—as would any good guide—some of the local history. This included, but was not limited to: the Tetons; "Beaver Dick" Leigh; and Jenny—Beaver Dick's "Geisha" wife, who, it should be noted, had been charged with carrying the family lodge poles from one location to another.

And I can understand if the whole account was a little too much for Fannie to digest at the time. There was the language barrier and all. But I still think that the only reason she refused to carry my *Italian*-made tripod was out of nationalistic pride.

"That's a Bogan," I tried to correct her (with a bad Italian accent). But she insisted.

"No, that bo-gus!"

She soon began to smell another rat—a "winterkill" field rat, combining with rotten egg smell—and so naturally looked in my direction.

"No, I didn't fart," I explained. "It's sulfur. It just means we're getting closer to the thermal basin."

"That Jenny person had a lake named after her," Fannie then blurted out of the blue.

"I'll see what I can do," I replied as she grudgingly agreed to carrying a small fanny-pack for me.

And I should mention here that it's a widely accepted unwritten regional rule that any would-be discoverer may in fact name some of the smaller backcountry mud features. These features (unlike, for instance, waterfalls), are exempt from the "thou shalt not name" dictate, only because they tend to disappear—sometimes overnight (along with their names)—to spring up elsewhere, just waiting to be rediscovered and renamed. And I like to use (an equally-capricious), pop culture for inspiration.

"What about this one," I asked as we reached the first small basin and examined one of its features. It kind of reminds me of you.

"That just mud puddle," Fannie said.

"No," I explained. "It used to be: Puddle O' Mud. But I hereby re-christen it: Fannie Got Backpack."

She wasn't terribly impressed. But I knew, having visited the area many times, that "Fannie Got Backpack" was, as of the previous week anyway, an active mud *geyser*, with intervals of about 30 minutes, and reaching a height of almost eight feet. But I wanted to surprise my guest. So I set my camera and tripod up right there—intending to return for the eruption. I then went about showing Fannie the rest of the basin, which included the following features:

- Primus (and its, "My Name is Mud" satellite mudpot),
- Betty Bloop,
- Buffalo Field Spring,
- Muddy Waters,
- and Harry Potter's Crock Pot.

This last one, for some reason, reminded me of my camera set-up back at "Fannie Got Backpack." So I led its namesake back to it, carefully tiptoeing through the steam, the spider threads, and the sun-bleached bison bones of the basin. It was even eerier than usual, thus setting a certain sorcerous mood. So naturally, when we got there, I made a big show of conjuring up apparitions—primarily Sulfurious, the infernal God of angry mudpots. And for Him, I used a nearby pitchstone phone.

But before I could even punch in the final digit, and more importantly, before I could tell my companion to reach into her fanny pack and pull out the pair of protective eyeglasses (round lenses and all)—"Fannie Got Backpack" erupted—all over us.

Needless to say, afterwards, Fannie had a few choice names for *me*, mostly in Japanese. And during the rest of our wanderings she refused to go near any of the mud features—not just the newly named: "Here's Mud in Your Eye."

"I got one in English," she finally said.

But I tried to ignore it all. Who knew what dark forces were at work churning within *her*? And I can only imagine the story told 100 years from now about how: Once upon a time, not far from the Oxbow Bend and massive Mt. Moran, lived the oxymoronically-monikered David "Beaver Peter" San, and his estranged friend Fannie. I just hope that—like all my mudpots—the name is as fleeting as the fame.

How to Bait a Ranger

Contrary to popular opinion, I don't have a problem with park rangers. I really don't. Oh, sure, there've been what I call situations, such as the overly documented "tip" from a well-intentioned health inspector (which resulted in a brief detainment); and the "crop" circle hoax in Hayden Valley (as yet unsolved); and the restricted-waters mushroom-flotation-device mix-up (more a shipping disaster than anything else). But by-and-large, our paths rarely even cross. When they do, though, it almost always involves some sort of food.

That could be because I'm a cook, or was one. Or it could be because rangers are always hungry—left, usually, to fend for themselves in ill-equipped government housing. But it's probably a combination of both.

The cooking job was for a private concessionaire in Yellowstone—specifically the general stores. And it was bad enough feeding *their* employees. But on certain special occasions—as a not-so-subtle public-relations ploy—rangers would be invited to sit down with us to "sup."

Such as when we had fish fries—fish fries of native cutthroat trout—trout donated by assorted said employees—employees who liked to angle—an angle that was only quasi-legal. And as Ranger ("Red") Smythe sat at the table (in the "sup" position), tossing skeleton after skeleton over his ungrateful shoulder, he turned to the "theme desert"—Gummi Fish—Gummi Fish floating belly-up in blueberry Jello—Jello that had set up a little too quickly—a set-up that was to inspire another kind of set-up, somewhere on down the road.

So after slamming the swell goop in one fell swoop Ranger Smythe reminded us all of various park regulations—regulations involving fish—fish that couldn't be kept if over 13 inches, or fished-for with live bait. It reminded me of the old saying that: "men with tape-measure esophagi shouldn't throw bones."

"And the case is still pending," the guest ranger announced, casting a suspicious eye in my direction, "as to the creator of that circle in Hayden Valley. But rest assured we *are* closing in. We've recently made a moulage from some nearby footprints."

It also occurred to me, come to think of it, that those who mix Plaster-of-Paris shouldn't cast an eye, suspicious or otherwise, in *any* direction . . . least of all in mine. They didn't call me the Teflon Chef because of my cookware.

And I couldn't help but notice from my dorm-room window "routine" flashlight checks of my vehicle in a desperate search for clues—clues that might involve rope, two-by-fours, Weed-Whackers, buoyant fungi, anything—anything that might incriminate me. But it was all to no avail. I even went so far as to "plant" very *con*trovertible prima facie evidence in my car (The Mutha'), just to mystify them further. A brochure for Kamp Kampf (a theme resort in northern Idaho), left on the front passenger seat, for instance, left *them* looking for trip-wires and *me* under continued observation. The box marked ACME Wolf Traps stashed overtly on the backseat was a personal favorite of mine. And Buffalo Branding Irons (bought from the same novelty store as the wolf traps), branded *me* a bad *seed*. And last but not least—leastwise according to my cohorts, Abel, Baker, and Charlie, were candy cigarettes—cigarettes sucked down on each end—sucked down so as to simulate tightly rolled joints of marijuana.

Abel, Baker, and Charlie ate my cooking too, a lot of it, but unlike the rangers, they actually lived in the dorm and *paid* for their board. In fact, Abel, Baker, and Charlie ate so much that it would make a person wonder—wonder about why they liked having attention diverted from them so much. Abel, Baker, and Charlie all considered *me* to be a friend—a very good friend.

And one night around midnight, after slurping down all the leftover Gummi Fish Jello—Jello that had somehow miraculously survived ranger Smythe—Abel spoke,

"Dude, thanks for letting us in the kitchen this late at night."

"Yeah, you're awesome," Charlie said!

"Shhh, I could get in trouble."

Baker having just returned from a solitary Australian-rules "soul search" (as he liked to call it), then found us in the kitchen,

"Suuuuuup!"

"That's right," Abel'd say. "Thas wha' were doin'. Dig in—I think there's still some of that nasty ol' Vegemite of yours left."

Baker's mouth began to water.

Charlie, on the other hand, had long since devoured *his* native kimchi—kimchi that hadn't been prepared *exactly* the way his grandmother had fixed it, using Chinese cabbage—cabbage that had been buried in the ground by the light of a new moon and left to spoil. It was a burial process, incidentally, that should have taken place *after* the fermentation stage—an odorous stage that would have been considered, even *under* ground, to be a blatant act of bear-baiting. And I say it *would* have been, because the ground turned out to be way too rocky for decent digging. But no one can say I didn't try.

"Whatcha' got planned for tomorrow's desert?" Baker'd then ask in his Aussie accent.

"Worms," I replied, "and topsoil."

I guess the Gummi Fish and previous day's ranger lecture had, to some degree, influenced my thinking, because I went on to described to them a matrix made of crushed Oreo cookies and chocolate pudding that looked remarkably like rich nitrogenized worm bedding—a bedding that would eventually sleep two to three full-sized Gummi Worms—worms that were amazingly realistic—all served, as a matter of course, in individual white Styrofoam containers, just like at the bait shop.

"Mmmmm . . ." Abel, Baker and Charlie all said in unison.

And as usual I over-prepped. Cooking for a hundred people, I only actually served about fifty on any given day, and no rangers were signed up to eat that given day. Still, it was chocolate. And I knew how much Molly (a cute co-worker of ours), liked chocolate (in almost any form), and how much the health inspector liked surprises. And then there was Manny.

Manny—a Uinta ground squirrel—had taken up residence inside my car's habitat-trail dashboard. And although I'd recently installed a contact lense case food-and-water dish especially for him (the diet was for his own good), Manny refused to use it. You see, he liked his chocolate too.

And my original idea was to lure the girl, not the squirrel, into my vehicle with something chocolaty. It worked pretty well too—at first.

But Molly wasn't "taking the bait" as often as she used to—although she *was* dating someone—someone outside dormitory circles—circles in which she routinely talked when questioned by me. And although I did have a lot of things going on in my car that particular summer, Molly was rarely one of them, and then only as a friend.

And being somewhat cynical, I first suspected Manny of having sabotaged the relationship. But I now realize that my car was simply not big enough for the both of them—Manny thinking that Molly wore too much Moleskin—Molly finally realizing that the chocolate "sprinkles" decorating the various deserts left in my car, weren't sprinkles at all, but merely the results of Manny's rather insincere efforts at "recycling" chocolate.

But being the ever-*optimistic* cynic, I always kept my car "loaded." *Someone* would eventually come around—if only Charlie, Baker, or Abel.

Abel would, of course, often be *dis*abled as per my nickname for him—Mayor Stoner. So would Charlie—aka Mr. Stash. Baker really didn't need a nickname.

But mostly I'd come around to them—after having first dropped them off at their favorite fishing hole—a "burn area" near the Firehole River. It was definitely a trip, if not technically a "bake run." More like a Baker, Abel and Charlie run—it was also my civic duty. Hey, park roads were scary enough without potentially inebriated drivers on them.

And it was during one such return trip that I just happened to get pulled over.

"Evening," ranger Smythe said as I automatically handed him my license and registration.

"Suuuuup?" Baker asked the ranger.

"Been fishing I see," Smythe then said, eying the rod cases. "Hopefully not after sunset."

"Stoner's the name," Abel giggled from the backseat, "S . . . t . . . o . . . "

"Any luck?" the ranger continued, feigning cordiality and ignoring Abel the best he could.

And as Baker filled ranger Smythe in on the day's catch, I couldn't help but notice someone in my rearview mirror. It was Molly—in the ranger car's passenger seat—a seating arrangement known in law enforcement circles as a ride-along—a ride-along configuration also known in seating circles as a situation—a present *tense* situation now reduced, sadly (for me anyway), to a *sat*uation.

"So you released all but *one*?" Smythe continued. "Where is it?"

"S . . . t . . . n . . . o . . ." Abel continued from the back seat, still *unable* to spell out his alias.

Smythe then *finally* began to get suspicious,

"I'm afraid I'm going to have to give you boys all a breathalyzer . . ." he started to say.

But at that point, somewhere between the "breathalyzer" and the "test," part of his statement, something or some *things* caught ranger Smythe's eye, diverting his attention even further. Those *things*, and the recollection of a report he received describing *me* out walking "by the light of a new moon," with a shovel, is, I'm guessing, what caused him to launch into one of his infamous lectures.

"I hope I don't have to remind you," he said, focusing his flashlight on the objects—shriveled, sun-baked, objects that lay half-in and half-out of a Styrofoam container on the dashboard, "that any natural resource harvested from within Park boundaries must be used or consumed immediately, lest you violate paragraph eight, section seven of the Park County possession rule . . ."

"Suuuuushie," Charlie then said volunteering his breath to the ranger.

". . .with the exception . . ." the ranger continued through clenched teeth, ". . . of fish."

And by then Molly had gotten out of the ranger car and had milled her way over to where she could more clearly observe the proceedings. And I, of course, didn't want to be outdone in front of her, so I took immediate action—action that kinda' got out of hand.

"What natural resources?" I asked, attempting to pull one of the less-withered worms from its bedding in one piece (but breaking off only about three inches instead). "I don't see no stinking resources."

And as you might expect, this act started out simple enough—an insecure hipster-wannabe's display of his "underground acumen" as per the rich tradition of evidence-disposal—but ended up more an attempt, I think, to appease Molly, than anything else, to perhaps prove to her that I, myself, would be willing to eat multi-fold Manny forms (of which, by the way, I detected many).

That, and there was a little matter of the desert having so thoroughly congealed that I couldn't just put the ingredients in question in my mouth to chew on with mock relish—but had to consume the mock relish as well, even offering a rapidly reddening ranger Smythe a small "clod" that had fallen in my lap.

"You really should store that stuff in little bygies," Baker chimed in, "like me Vegemyte. Don't want it to get stale do ya' moite?"

Ranger Smythe, at that point realizing it *was* yet another stalemate, just gave up, shaking his head derisively while uttering something under his breath—something that sounded like, "Dirtbags . . . buncha' dumb dirtbags."

Come to think of it, it sounded *exactly* like that. He then walked back to his cruiser and left by himself, to be heard from again only at certain supper times.

"I don't know what I ever saw in that guy anyway," Molly said as we all rode away together. "Did you know he claimed there were whole fields of illegal crops being harvested from the backcountry?"

"That's what all that confiscated weed'll do to you . . ." Abel stated, ". . . make you paranoid."

"And that's what *I* call: the *pot* calling the marijuana *green*," I replied.

"Huh?" the backseat replied in unison.

"Speaking of which," Molly continued, "I can't believe you thought to eat that *other* 'evidence' too."

"They did make kind of a realistic crunching sound didn't they?"

"And what were your exact words afterwards?" she asked, recounting the episode. "Nothing goes with worms like roaches?"

"Something like that."

Thus we drove on into the night. And with an ever-more admiring Molly back in place (in her ex position), me behind the wheel chomping on a big ol' bubble gum blunt (né: cigar), and Manny still manning the point—all seemed right in Wonderland.

And that Charlie, Baker, and Abel were all able to fit into my car's backseat—what with the large strap-on feet and Weed Whackers (among other things)—is a wonder in and of itself.

But we knew we had to eventually jettison something. So we dropped off Abel, Baker, and Charlie—to be picked up later, of course, in a kind of twi-night bake-run doubleheader. It was a good situation—a good situation all around—one that in dirtbag circles is known as hanging out—hanging out in crop circles.

Anatomy of a Bear Jam

W hat a *day* I was having! It started out as usual during that time period, with my slithering out of the womb—the sleeping "birth" portion of the *Wheeled Womb* that is—also known as: The Log, or my Toyota Sequoia. I slithered head-first from the cramped sleeping area to the relatively spacious driver's area, reached up from there with my non-dominant foot and found the ignition switch with my toes. The engine roared to life.

It was a *good* day. Any day was a good one that didn't start with my having to cut the sleeping bag drawstring tangled around my neck. Reality then slapped me into full consciousness as I righted myself and noticed *the notice* attached to my windshield. I snatched the slip of paper, and skewered it with all the others on the vehicle's built-in spindle before backing out of the parking space. Authorities can't legally ticket you for "camping out of bounds" if said authority figures don't make direct visual contact with the actual person "camping" out of bounds—or hear the actual "camper" snoring (aka sawing logs).

And there's no vehicle's sleeping berth more soundproof than the Wheeled Womb (aka Log). Furthermore, you'd think, of all people, *park rangers* would be more concerned with saving trees than effectively killing them by issuing unnecessary, unenforceable warnings.

And as I drove on down the road, I naturally couldn't help but think about the one time I actually visited Sequoia National Park. There, amid the giant living trees, could be found a "log cabin," or "tree house," if you will. This, "tree cabin" was in the form of a single downed hollow sequoia—about as prefab as you can get—or so you'd think.

And in this downed hollow tree once lived—not an elf—as you may suppose, but an actual flesh and blood man, a mountain man. The man's name: Tharp; The abode's name: Tharp's Log. I recalled gazing through the abode's windows and seeing rough-hewn furniture, some wood-framed bas-relief art pieces, and a stone fireplace that Tharp had built into the side of the log. I, of course, felt an instant kinship with Tharp even though at the time of my visit to Sequoia National Park, I merely lived in a smoke spewing AMC Pacer (albeit a *wood-paneled* AMC Pacer), and not the Toyota Sequoia.

Now no one knows too much about him, but I assume that conventional thinking has it that Tharp moved into the place *after* it was hollow. I, for one, don't like conventional thinking. I like to think Tharp was a genius, an unconventional thinker himself. I like to think that Tharp started by building the fireplace and chimney into one end of the *non*-hollow log, and then created his living space as he needed firewood. Perhaps he even ended up burning some of the homemade furniture when he ran out of room.

It took him two full winters just to get to that point though. And if there's any justice at all, the backstory would be that during construction Tharp slept just outside the log under a canvass lean-to until there was enough room for him to get inside the log and actually start chipping away. The lean-to's name: Tharp's Tarp.

Yes, you do tend to think of weird things like that when you live in your vehicle for long periods of time. And in as much as Tharp had a log that was *hollowed* out, I had a Toyota Sequoia that was—*tricked* out.

It was tricked out mainly with the JohnStar navigation system. It all has something to do with odor-sensors located in some sort of mechanical housing under the hood. I don't know, I'm not all that tech savvy, nor (as you may have guessed), am I all that familiar with housing in general. But the *outhouse* to which my JohnStar guided me this particular morning was one I knew well. I knew its insides and its outs.

That's maybe because I might have possibly crawled onto its roof another morning—about ten years earlier—to get a better view of a grizzly bear that ultimately refused to strike a decent pose. The outhouse in question was, of course, located in prime Yellowstone grizzly habitat—on Dunraven Pass to be exact. Still is. And although I waited for the bear to cooperate for perhaps an hour, cameras at the ready, all I got out of it was an ironic (and fairly *in*decent) picture of a bear squatting in the woods—which turned out to be underexposed anyway. Pretty standard for me back then.

But, much like the half-dozen or so very bemused outhouse *users*, all of that is beneath me now. You can't really call yourself a nature photographer (let alone a wilderness photographer), if you're doing your shooting anywhere near a road or a building. And so unless it's just a spectacular, once in a lifetime photo opportunity, I can proudly say that I no longer contribute to the culture of roadside photography.

And I didn't plan to this particular day either. I was simply taking the opportunity (after taking care of my in-house outhouse business), to organize my photo equipment in the empty parking space furthest upwind of the privy, when a compact sedan with a badly crumpled fender pulled up along side of me.

A giant camouflaged camera lens and giant bearded face then poked out of the drivers'-side window.

"He come back for more of his grub I reckon, huh?" he sort of asked me.

"Huh?" I sort of responded.

"The griz—ol' 367—he come back for his meal cache? Ain't that what brung you here?" he asked, this time pointing to my tripod.

"I . . . uh, don't think so." I said. "My JohnStar navigation system is what brought me here. And now I'm just organizing my . . ."

The camouflaged man stopped me in mid-sentence, as other vehicles began materializing from the thin mountain air. He cracked the door of his Pop-n-Fresh car and oozed out of it, olive drab biscuit dough spilling onto the pavement. He then gathered all his photo gear before explaining,

"A bunch of us was watching ol' 367 drag a cow elk carcass down into that draw yesterday. Three rangers were needed just for the traffic jam alone. I was the first to spot him though . . . a big ol' silvertip boar . . . maybe three years old—possibly four."

"Is that so," I asked?

"Yeah, and you should have been here. The light was real purdy then. Not like now. And they was much closer to the road at the time, probability no more than two, two hunnert feet. I got some great pictures of it all."

"Of course you did," I said, always a little jealous.

"Then he started eatin' on her," the man continued, "and when he finally got his fill, he started burying the carcass—as they'll usually do. Then he walked off into the woods where he kept an eye on his grub pile. Anyway, the sun was down by then—and I already got *my* picture—so I figured I'd go back to camp and try again at sunup."

"Where're you camping?" I asked. "If you don't mind my asking."

The man lowered his head and muttered something under his breath, something that sounded like, "Best Western," and, "West Yellowstone."

Aha, camping *in*-bounds.

And apparently a lot of others had gotten up early and driven in from West Yellowstone or Gardiner Montana to "try again at sunup."

They were mostly all the same too. They talked in a typical western movie language that Tharp's crustiest of old sidekicks would have had a hard time understanding. Most had white beards or goatees and were dressed head to toe in camouflage. Their photographic equipment was also camouflaged—in stark contrast to the bright shiny automobiles parked directly behind them.

And I can't say that I, myself, didn't own any camouflage. I had a single pair of jungle "Combo-Combat" boots—in stark contrast with *my* bright shiny *Salvation* Army thrift-store windbreaker.

I bought the boots, incidentally, at a quaint little (non-salvation), army-surplus store just outside Langley, Virginia called Smudgepots R Us.

So I had at least a little bit in common with the crusty-old-codger-would-be-wildlife-photographer-types at the early morning bear jams. But I also had a little in common with the other types—the lady types.

These lady types, by far the minority, looked less like Vietnam vets on a camping trip, and more like another kind of soldier, one on leave from the *Greenpeace* army. And mainly our *hair style* is what *we* had in common. What came out of their mouths was also a different language—sometimes Latin, like, "Ursus Arctos Horribillus."

"Ursus Arctos Horribillus . . ." the crusty old codger who first talked to me said, mocking one of the nature-loving lady-types. And later, in response to the lack of activity around the buried carcass, ". . . what we have here is an Ursus Arctos *Belly*-full-us. Haw haw!"

But that all changed, as someone from behind the long lineup of tripods noticed something moving, and shouted,

"There he is, he's come back fer breakfast."

"And look—there's a *wolf*!" someone else shouted.

The sound of countless shutters clicking simultaneously was deafening as "367" (if that *was* his real number), and a *coyote* independently approached the buried carcass from different angles. I don't know what number the coyote had been assigned, but *his* definitely would have been *up* (like the elk's), had he not veered away from the carcass at the last second. And they always do. The bear, after staring down the coyote (with the most intimidating look he could muster at that time of day), plopped down on top of the mound of buried elk and didn't move again for at least as long as I was there.

And that gave everyone a chance to do what they do best—talk. The codger-types would try to out codger one another; while the naturalist-wannabe lady-types would try to out-granola each other. But they all had one common language—that of one-upsmanship . . . regarding cameras and camera equipment, not to mention their exploits with said gear.

"Whatcha' workin' with," would be the all-too common question at these (what amounted to), social gatherings?

"Oh, I just got the Nikon Blawblawblaw with the Sigma Blawblaw lens and, of course, a 2x tele-converter," was just one typical mind-numbing answer.

"You?"

"Oh, I just got the Canon Blawblawblah with the in-body Blah-reduction. And I bought the Blawblaw-blawblawblaw blawblawblah lens just for this trip. It came in real handy too the other day up in the Lamar Valley when a mother fox picked up her young un' by the scruff of it's yada yada and . . ."

"I didn't even know yada yadas *had* scruff," I interrupted at the risk of getting drawn into the conversation,

"What you workin' with?" someone, of course, then asked *me*.

"Oh, these are just 'Combo-Combats,'" I said pointing down at my camouflaged feet, "I bought 'em at Smudgepots R Us . . ."

Their stares then prompted me to explain,

". . . but that's just the *model* of boot I got. I think the company that makes them is the Cammo-Toe company. This particular model has the combined features of having anti-toe jam properties, *and* a camera lens built into each toe—hence, the Cammo-Toe Jam Cam. They dare you to find the lens in the steel toe. It's that well hidden . . ."

This, of course, prompted more stares and even more explanation.

". . . come to think of it," I said, "Smudgepots R Us may have been a *CIA*-surplus store. In any case, the twelve mega-pixels (twenty-four if you count both feet), came in real handy when I was shooting scruff over by the naturalist lady-types a few seconds ago . . ."

I went on like this for probably way too long, mentioning Lindy England and Guantanamo Bay toward the end. And I'm sure to the hard core photographer it all sounded like so much blaw blaw blaw-blawblaw, but they were spared to some extent when ten o'clock rolled around.

Ten o'clock, I should explain, is about when the typical-tourist crowd will find the typical bear jam.

Typical-tourists, as opposed to *photo*-tourists, travel in family-packs, thus taking them much longer to get going in the morning. And they just carry around un-camouflaged point-and-shoot cameras. Okay, they carry around their un-camouflaged children too, sometimes on their shoulders, to get better views—of bears—at bear jams.

And many of the kids, if they and their families went into any of the Visitor Centers in Yellowstone, are, or have been, enrolled in what's known as the Junior Ranger program. Some have simply been graduated and have gone on to the more mundane Junior Desk Job program. But some have rolls of yellow police tape. I don't know if this tape is actually issued to them (along with the badges and Smokey Bear hats), but I do know that at least one kid had a big roll of it, and was using it that morning (rightfully so), to keep us all at least one hundred yards away from the bear.

And in backing off, I kind of lost my place in the line of tripods and was thus further away from the crusty codger to whom I first spoke. But I could still hear him. He was bragging to everyone about having been the first to spot the bear and elk. And that's when one of the Junior Rangers at the scene asked him if he saw the actual kill. Shortly after that discussion, the plainclothes Junior Ranger began examining the codger's crumpled fender, even pulling what appeared to be a hair-sample from the grill, a hair sample perhaps from a cow elk.

Another of the Junior Rangers started paying closer attention to my Toyota and its antenna—with all the notices spindled on it—before pulling out his non-issue Walkie-Talkie. Those events, respectively, caused Crusty Codger to quiet down some, and *me* to get away from it all.

And I really just needed to go on a hike somewhere—anywhere—to get the taste of roadside photography out of my mouth. I knew just the place too. It was a place crawling with bears—backcountry bears: Turbid Lake.

About a 14-mile round-trip hike, I'd been to Turbid Lake twice. Neither time did I see a single human being—a perfect people-palette-cleanser. But I also didn't see any bears. That's not to say I didn't see any sign of them. I once turned my ankle after having accidentally stepped into a particularly deep grizzly paw print, and I once had to take a detour when a particularly large pile of fresh scat blocked the trail to the lake. The signage was *everywhere*. So I knew it was just a matter of time—if I walked quietly enough—before I'd eventually see the source of said sign.

And *walked quietly enough*, is the operative phrase. Junior and senior rangers alike advise hikers to make a lot of noise while using Yellowstone's trails. They'll tell you to shout out, "Hey Yogi!" or something like that every couple-hundred yards in order *not* to surprise any such cutlass-clawed *non*-cartoon animal that might be in the area. A surprised bear, you see, is one that is more likely to panic and run toward you instead of away. This deliberate making-of-noise is very sound advice.

Someone who buys his camera/hiking gear from CIA-surplus stores and bargain basements, however, is someone who is less likely to heed such sound advice—*and* more likely to purchase five-year-old outdated pepper spray from the same sources.

And I had this canister of bear deterrent strapped conveniently to one of my tripod's legs (while, incidentally, *whispering* "Hey Yogi" every hundred yards or so), when I saw my first non-roadside bear of the day.

About a half-mile from Turbid Lake—about fifty yards away from *me*—could be seen a grizzled hump on the other side of a hill. The rest of the bear, seconds later, could be seen cresting the hill, silhouetted against and/or blotting out the sun—not to mention *sauntering in my direction*. *Thirty-five* yards away from me, I assumed the bear saw me frantically setting up my tripod, and still didn't much care—except maybe to *eat* me.

Twenty-five yards away, however, the bear definitely *heard* the Velcro ripping open on my pepper spray holster, and saw me for the first time—or maybe just my bulging eyes. She jumped a little (having been surprised!), and—much to my relief—turned and ran *away*.

I later determined that the bear needed glasses (Morty Seinfeld-sized glasses), and didn't much care herself, for the sound that Velcro made—as it may have accompanied her having previously been sprayed. Who knows?

So I ventured onward, even though the bear *had* run off in the direction of my destination—Turbid Lake. But who cared? I had the Kryptonite. Only this time I stuffed it in my coat pocket instead of strapping it to my tripod leg. I would be hand-holding my Pentax Blawblawblaw with the blawblaw blawblawblaw lens from here on out.

And I must say that when you're an old loser like me, living out of your vehicle with no signature bear photo (backcountry or front-country), to speak of—you tend to take certain chances. I knew that Turbid Lake, an ancient hydrothermal explosion crater, was rimmed with hot springs and mud pots. And with the cool temperatures of September the steam from these thermal features would be thick and eerie-looking—typical Yellowstone—just the way I like it. A grizzly walking through this miasma would be one of the coolest shots ever.

So when I saw most likely the same bear at the edge of a good-sized boiling mud spring I almost couldn't believe my eyes. I was roughly 100 yards away and took pictures of the bear walking all around this thermal feature, occasionally sticking her head over the roiling mud and into the steam—as if getting a facial.

Incidentally, that's how I knew the bear was a girl. No self-respecting *guy*-bear would want to hang out at a spa, natural or otherwise. Granted, there's no better mud-packs this side of Baden-Baden, but still . . .

And the pictures I got of her were far from award-winners. And certainly non of them were the coolest shot ever. But I am sure they were better than the ones I would have gotten had I stayed back at the roadside bear jam—because they were uniquely mine.

Pores sufficiently open, the bear then walked off into the woods and kept walking—at least as far as I could tell. I backed off too. I needed time to reflect.

What a *day* I was having!

And when you're an old loser living out of your vehicle you also have a lot of time on your hands, and not much to go back to. But that's what *one* of the voices in my head was advising me—to head back to my vehicle. I'd pressed my luck enough as it was.

But you don't get to where I was by listening to the common sense voices in your head, you listen to the ones telling you to walk on down to the mud pot to see if you might be able to photograph fresh grizzly prints in the surrounding soil.

And so I compromised. I waited about an hour before doing the latter, giving the bear sufficient time to clear out before looking for the prints. But I couldn't find any! How on earth, I thought to myself, could an animal that large leave behind absolutely no prints—in fairly soft mud? The voice in my head (the one that was still speaking to me anyway), didn't have an answer either. And as I stood amid the steam, taking in this wholesome hellish atmosphere, brimstone to the left of me, pitchstone to the right, I also noticed the quiet.

Sure, there was the soft rumble of churning mud and the hissing of countless fumaroles, but that to me is tantamount to the sound of a soft breeze murmuring through the Lodgepole pines—a ".05" on a 100 point decibel scale.

Imagine then a "1500" on that scale, a high-pitched death-scream breaking that relative silence. On second thought—don't. It's the absolute worst sound a human could possibly imagine in that setting. And it sent me skyward.

And on my way down from this fear-induced record-breaking vertical leap, I saw the culprit, the creature, the hound from Hell that made it—it was a coyote, a single puny coyote, on the other side of the pitchstone.

On the other side of the *brimstone*, however (still on my descent), I noticed the nearsighted grizzly—only three or four hundred *feet* away!—and walking toward me again, apparently this time to investigate the ruckus.

But thankfully the pocket that housed my pepper spray was *also* held together with Velcro. And my ripping it open to fumble for the spray was all it took to alert the bear to my presence. It was either that or the sound of all the *brown* being sucked from every third hair follicle on my body—not exactly a great audio experience either.

But again, thankfully, this is when the animal stopped, jumped a little herself (at the sight of me, blanching), and ran *away*—but only for about a hundred yards this time.

She then turned and glared at me, as if tired of doing middle-distance wind sprints. I, in turn, took that opportunity to practice *my* new event—the 100-yard quivering backwards shuffle. And it led me to a fairly high point at the edge of a ravine where I felt relatively safe.

After regaining my composure, at least somewhat, I set up my tripod and again started taking pictures.

The pictures of the sky, however, that I got after I executed my triple-axle backwards twisting somersault into the *ravine* routine (having gone from field events to diving and gymnastics in mere seconds), which occurred as a result of the bear just then having decided to charge me, were useless to anyone, except maybe to me—as a memento of my having survived that fun filled day.

Similarly, the upside-down blurry pictures I accidentally got of the berry bushes, the very prickly berry bushes, into which I dismounted upon bouncing off the boulder halfway down the ravine (and I must say I was surprised at how much spring my old ribs still had in them), will also be filed under the category of "Memory Snapshots" (as if the pepper-spray canister-marks didn't leave *enough* of a lasting impression—on my ribs).

The voices in my head were now in complete agreement. "Get out," they said!

And, indeed, the day pretty much ended for me right there, with my slithering *feet* first from a rotting log at the base of the berry bushes, which ultimately did not (and I thank the bear to this day for having mercy on me), did *not* serve as my wooden (un-wheeled) tomb.

Oh sure, there was also the long walk back to my Sequoia where I saw a half-dozen other grizzlies. And there was the time *during* that walk, when "The Bear *Whisperer*" became "The Bear *Hollerer*," shouting "Hey Yogi!" every *ten seconds*. And there was that unfortunate time much too far down the trail when I realized my vehicle's ignition keys had, at one time, been with my pepper spray in my breast pocket—but weren't currently. And finally there was that wonderful time after having retrieved the keys from the berry bushes and having walked back through all that bear country when I reached my vehicle at the trailhead. The end . . .

. . . oh wait a minute, okay, there was also the drive back to wherever I was "camping" that night, which brought me right past the earlier bear jam—which was still going on! The codgers were still there too, most of them anyway. Only they were now sitting around in lawn chairs behind their tripods, and passing around donuts. And so I decided to *intentionally* stop in this time—to tell them about my day.

"Hey, where'd you go, Cammo-Toe?" the first crusty codger asked upon seeing me. "You missed all the excitement. But I'd expect as much from a greenhorn like you. Haw haw!"

"I don't know." I started to say before being interrupted. "I had a little excitement of my own. I was out hiking to . . ."

". . . seems ol' 367 was rootin' around in the elk carcass lookin'

133

for a liver or something," the codger continued, "when he happened upon what I'm guessing was the gall bladder instead. Must have been plumb *full* of bile too, 'cause when it popped, it got all over the bear. And you shoulda' seen the expression on that guy's face, all covered with that nasty green stuff. That's when I snapped the shutter. Got a great picture."

"Of course you did," I said slipping into an empty chair.

"Ain't been so much as an eye-twitch since then," another codger said. "We been watching him sleep on what's left of the carcass for the past three hours. Good thing there's an outhouse close by."

Another codger then offered me a donut.

"Sorry, the only ones left are the key lime-filled Bismarcks—fer obvious reasons."

"Thanks. Don't mind ifin' I do," I said. "I'm hungry as a b'ar."

"Say, I forgot to ask you where *your* base camp is," the first codger then asked me.

"I got me a little log home," I responded in my best Best Western on-demand western-movie-voice. "It's not too far from here either."

"Oh, a local," the codger then said. "Lucky you."

"Lucky indeed," I said, "lucky indeed."

The Airport Challenge

Fear of public speaking. We're all aware of it. Most of us have it—including me. Much less known, however, is the fear of public *sleeping*, which I also have. Okay, maybe it's completely unknown to everyone but me. But somehow I doubt it. There has to be others out there, maybe even a support group, a very uptight, boring, sleep-inducing support group . . . the potential cure.

And while fear of public *speaking* can now be cured, or at least alleviated, by simply imagining your audience naked, fear of public *sleeping* is only exacerbated by this notion, or more precisely, dreaming about these imagined naked people (mainly the better-looking females), and then uttering the word "exacerbate" in your sleep for all to hear.

ATTENTION: Please keep all luggage and packages with you at all times until they are checked. Unattended luggage and packages are subject to inspection. This

announcement will be made every hour, on the hour—
so get used to it.

But mainly I don't want anyone *watching me drool* while I'm dreaming about *naked people*, or listening to me snore. And my first search for a public sleeping phobia support group (PSPSG), came up short in Singapore—way short.

And I know what you're thinking, there's no shortage of uptight people anywhere, especially there. But Singapore, for one reason or another (which might become obvious later on), has to rank right up there, perhaps second only to Mexico, as harboring the largest number of public-sleeper cells in the world.

And I photographed many of the actual sleepers themselves—head back, mouth agape, cheeks vibrating with every deep halitosis-filled breath. And I know, it was a total invasion of privacy. But it was so much fun. I got them in their natural habitats too—on the train, in the food court, and at Karaoke Night (ironically during the song "Dream Weaver").

So it serves me right, when at a party I attended with a Singaporean friend of mine (which I assumed would end at maybe 1:00 am), that I was the only one *not* sacked out on various pieces of furniture, or at least the only one not sacked out who wasn't interested in a lively game of Mahjong, or a lovers' quarrel conducted by two fifteen-year-old "lovers." And the way I figured it, my Karmic debt had been paid off at around 4:00 am, when the "lovers' quarrel" began to heat up and the first ashtray was thrown. When the statue of Buddha was thrown, I realized my best bet would be to be *like* the Buddha, and just sit there and take it, collecting Karma credits, at least until my ride—Shawn—took all his buddies' money at the Mahjong table, which he eventually did, at around *7:00 am.*

Months had passed since then, but I once *again* found myself fearing to fall asleep while waiting for a ride—this time at Omaha's Eppley Airport (a much better place, I might add, to while away the night than at a Singaporean house party). And I decided right then and there, to turn a perceived negative into an actual positive.

You see, I'd always wanted to write a story that would increase awareness of public sleeping phobias. What better time to do that? And I always wanted to include Thomas Mangelsen—fellow Nebraskan—in one of my little stories. What better *place* for *that*? Thomas Mangelsen, if you don't already know, is a hugely successful nature photographer (as opposed to me), and his pictures—equally huge prints—are displayed just about everywhere, including, of course, the Omaha airport, directly behind where I sat writing this very story.

> ATTENTION: Please keep all luggage and packages with you at all times until they are checked. Unattended luggage and packages are subject to inspection. This announcement will be made every hour on the hour. Some of you are able sleep through it.

The challenge, therefore, was to finish this story before my ride was scheduled to arrive—only six more airport announcements from that point forward—and, for one reason or another (which might become obvious later on), to do it all *unplugged*.

Sure, I had my laptop with me. And sure, there was an electrical outlet behind where I sat (just below the life-sized portrait of Mangelsen). But I instead pulled from one of my bulging cargo pants pockets a tattered piece of paper that had the words, "Please drive me to the Camellia Hotel" translated into Chinese; and pulled from my other pocket a ballpoint pen. I would do this "old-school," as they say—on the backs of various slips of paper.

A similar note pulled from my coat pocket listed the Stone Forest (near the city of Kunming), as a destination. Yes, my trip that year included Singapore, but this area around Kunming China was my more recent excursion—roughly 32 hours ago—32 *sleepless* hours from the time I started putting pen to paper in Omaha.

And it's difficult to describe China's Stone Forest without using the word *fairy*. So I won't. It's a fantastic labyrinth of weathered rock formations almost on the scale of Bryce Canyon—only consisting of spiky, harder-to-erode limestone. And if you don't know what Bryce Canyon looks like, come to the Omaha airport and look at one of Tom Mangelsen's photos of it—there's a huge one, across from where I sat.

Another difference between Bryce Canyon and the Stone Forest is that the paths between the rock pillars in the Stone Forest are much more narrow—sometimes even difficult for a normal sized person to squeeze through. In addition to that, there are "man-made" steps and stairways built throughout. Top it all off with twisted vines and other examples of creeping vegetation partly obscuring openings to numerous caves and small odd-shaped grottoes and you have a place where—I don't know—you might imagine *fairies* living.

> ATTENTION: Please keep all luggage and packages with you at all times until they are checked. Unattended luggage and packages are subject to inspection. Hey, Thomas Mangelsen would have the decency to do that.

Running out of space on my sheet of paper, I then pulled from my back pocket another one, only this one had the words, "Please drive me to the Dwarf Kingdom," translated into Chinese (for any taxi driver who might want to read it).

The Dwarf Kingdom (try miming that to your average professional Chinese travel translator), is a real place—I swear. It's on the *other* side of Kunming, though, and can be described a bit more succinctly—it's a little-people theme park. Google it if you don't believe me. It's made up of diminutive Chinese people living in mushroom-shaped prefab housing. They come out twice daily dressed in elaborate costumes to dance and perform acrobatic feats for the visiting public. And think what you will of their situation—exploitative or enabling—it's definitely not a dignified way to live.

138

And I never made it there. I ran out of time. But I am ashamed to say that I thought of coming back another year and hiring a few of the little people to run around the Stone Forest and let me photograph them there. And I repeat, I am ashamed of that notion. But I'd like to see Mangelsen get shots like that.

But the world is filled with too many indignities as it is, and too much suffering. People are people, regardless of our size, geographical location, or sleep habits—except for maybe the Japanese. *They* might be *better* than the rest of us.

And the phrase "turning Japanese" shouldn't come to mind in my attempt to be more stoic (that would be crass). But as my plane flew over this island nation on my long way back to Nebraska—on March 17th, 2011—a few short days after the earthquake, tsunami, and resultant nuclear crisis there, I, like most people, couldn't help but admire how the Japanese people as a whole had been coping. I wanted to be more like them.

And undoubtedly, they will come back—soon—perhaps even becoming the world leader in renewable energy-cell technology. But at the moment I was just glad to be in a country known for private sleeper cells.

> ATTENTION: Please keep all luggage and packages with you at all times until they are checked. Unattended luggage and packages are subject to inspection. Oh, and you're getting sleepy, very sleepy.

And my little gesture of "unplugging" (and thus re-purposing a paper product), was just that—a gesture. I'd still have to retype this into my laptop. Furthermore, I really should've been taking public transportation back to my temporary residence in Nebraska. But who knows, I might start working the conservation side of the street some day. Every little platitude helps.

And as I drifted into a slight trance—resting my eyes—I could almost hear Thomas Mangelsen laughing. I could almost hear Thomas

Mangelsen laughing while reading this very piece over my shoulder, this piece as written on a drool-stained slip of paper. Sure, it could have been the content he was laughing at. But I doubt it. I'm guessing it was the sound of my snoring.

Mushroom & Bored

What prompted us to try it, we'll never know—or I should say *I'll* never know. In the murky world of mind control and/or "memory manipulation" you're lucky if *anyone* knows. And it seems that any*thing* goes.

But I do remember my friend of that summer, William J. "Bill" Bryan III recounting to me his thrilling escape from Camp Camphor—a particularly insidious offshoot of Kamp Kamph. It's something a person doesn't soon forget. You see at Camp Camphor Bill said they would primarily mine camph. But they also played a lot of volleyball. It sounded just awful. And it's how I came to paint mushrooms.

I started out working in magic marker (with my magic mushroom marker), drawing clean, simple lines on a puffball. And for all you non-funguphiles out there, a puffball is a type of mushroom—a wild mushroom that can, and often will, grow to the size of a bas-ketball. I've seen (and even served), them that big. They're fairly common too, especially after a steady week-long rain. Most puff-balls, though, are about the size of a volleyball. And I've found that a medium-tipped Sharpie works best for reproducing the Voit or Spaulding logo.

Imagine then the *performance*-art generated upon the deft substitution of "puff," for "volley." The performance *artist* would sometimes then go off script, improvising to the effect that the mushrooms in his or her omelet were even more rubbery than usual. But these people were always jawing like that—at least when *I* cooked for them.

The real performance art was served up at the volleyball court, where my canvas (a perfectly dried work of art itself), never made it over the net, mushroom spoors perhaps still floating through the server's corneal fluid to this day.

Performance-art-*appreciation*, I might add (as an aside out), really should be taught at the Yellowstone Institute.

My education concerning mushrooms that summer, though, came mostly from Bill Bryan III, who taught me the above volleyball trick. But having been a longtime cook for the employees of a Yellowstone Park general store, I already knew just about everything I wanted to know about mushrooms, like, for instance, the type of "soil" in which they sometimes grow; and—because I had to so thoroughly clean this "soil" from the mushrooms by soaking them in a large sink of water—I also knew of their extreme buoyancy.

This then brings me full circle back to what has been dubbed, "The Attempt" (by park historians), which, incidentally, has only a slight connection to volleyball. And that connection was said volleyball server: Eva Prawn.

Eva (if that *is* her real name), was also *my* server—my octogenarian ex-third-reich-olympic athlete (or so she bragged), server. Her job, among other things, was to dish out the breakfast I cooked—some sort of thick cornmeal fluid *that* particular morning. And that same particular morning, perhaps because of all the strenuous volleyball-related activity the previous night (mainly *her* running after *me* in a blind rage), the normally punctual Eva had yet to show up for work. So I went to knock on her dorm room door.

I started with a light tapping, not knowing of her habit of keeping the door to her room unlocked and unlatched. And I have to say it's not totally outside the realm of possibility that the fastidious Fraulein also hired a team of freelance German engineers (probably from Idaho Falls)—to regularly service the hinges. Because at my first few taps, the door swung all the way open, in complete silence, to reveal a vision of Eva standing by her bed—stretching—and rubbing the sleep (or something else), out of her eyes.

She was dressed in what I later discovered was something commonly called—by the greatest generation (of women)—a pantie girdle, a matching pantie girdle and *bra*. The silence, of course, was then replaced with a rather high pitched, cornmeal-curdling, scream.

And it was only later, during that awkward period after she eventually entered the kitchen, that I came to the realization that "The Scream" (as it's been dubbed by park historians), was so loud that even the near-deaf Eva complained about it.

"Haven't you ever seen The Graduate?" she asked me as I dumped the curdled mass of cornmeal into the garbage disposal and started over with oatmeal. "Dustin Hoffman never screamed bloody murder."

And it was only later that I learned that traumatic experiences such as these, can, and often will, make you a better candidate for mind control, a post-hypnotic suggestion possibly being in the form of the details proffered to me later regarding what *she* deemed "sexy-but-practical foundation garments."

And I might counter that Dustin Hoffman never had to look at what appeared—at first glance anyway—to be bulging cattle-truss seams.

"The Attempt," though, came about only after "Bill" (if that *is* his real name), recounted for the umpteenth time his thrilling escape down the Salmon River from the Idaho concentration cult in which he *said* he was previously held captive.

"Concentraaaaate," he'd say. "Concentrate on my eyes as I retell the story."

143

And it didn't help matters that Ranger Smythe had been "guest eater" at lunch again that day, and that he had given to the employees his requisite lecture regarding rules and regulations—float tubes on Yellowstone's rivers being the point-of-emphasis that particular meal.

But Ranger Smythe also went into his standard spiel about harvesting Yellowstone's flora, "vitch iss verboten . . ." he'd say with a German accent before tossing a sautéed mushroom in the air, ". . . unless, of course, you're eating them 'as-you-go.'"

The mushroom then fell (as if from a German Panzer unit), into his London Tunnel-of-a-mouth.

"Or *doing* them 'as you go,'" I added just to be a drug-cultured smart-aleck, whereupon the humorless ranger began eyeing me with his usual suspicion.

"Or *utilizing* them 'as you go,'" Bill (if that's his real name), added somewhat enigmatically, while still eyeing me.

Eva eyed me as well, before striking a seductive pose.

It was enough to send a guy into a deep, deep trance.

And I don't remember a thing after that. At least I *didn't*, until I got help.

So now, all I can say is that I'm glad that the company for which I worked offered employee counseling, and that the counselor in question had taken the necessary correspondence courses in memory regression techniques, and that, last but not least, she offered me the full transcripts of the session.

And I should also mention that it's true, one cannot hypnoprogram a person into doing something he or she wouldn't normally be inclined to do—like, for instance, being the first person to legally float a full ten-mile stretch of the Firehole River in order to achieve a certain measure of Yellowstone immortality. But who *wouldn't* be inclined to do that? One might *not* be inclined, however, to release the transcripts to the public in fear of retribution.

But the way I figure it, the conspirators couldn't do anything worse than what they'd already done to me in Eva's dorm room. So here, reproduced below is the for-the-most-part-unedited transcript of our session:

Counselor: Now tell me, what is this "attempt" you've been mumbling about?

Subject (in a monotone): Not sure. All I know is . . . must sneak down to the kitchen . . . must sneak down and make PB&J sandwich.

C: Why is that?

S: For lunch. Now I remember—bag lunch for tomorrow's attempt.

C: Tell me more.

S: Getting sleepy . . .

C: But I already put you in a trance . . .

S: It was past my bedtime. I *remember* getting sleepy . . . set alarm for 3:00 am.

C: Okay, so what happens after you wake up?

S: I remembered having had a dream. Did you know that you have really weird dreams when sleeping while hypnoprogrammed? I think I dreamed I was dreaming that I was hypnotized to dream that I was in a trance. What do you think it means counselor?

C: Never mind the dream. So you're awake now, but still hypnotized—by someone besides me. What are you thinking?

S: Thinking raid . . . must raid pantie drawer . . . door always unlatched . . . she won't hear a thing . . . must make pantie girdle raid.

C: Go on.

S: (Panicking) No pantie girdle! What the . . . no pantie girdle anywhere in the drawer . . . (calming down) wait . . . must check dirty clothes hamper. Aha! A pantie girdle—and bra . . . very lacy, very large, very sheer bra . . .

C: Okay, so you've located some woman's underwear. What do you do next?

S: Wake Bill . . . must knock on door and wake Bill Bryan III.

C: Does this get weirder. Because I'm just a counselor. I can't . . .

S: No weirdness . . . no. Bill drives us in my car to Fountain Flats . . . Firehole river nearby . . . get out . . . hunt for puffball

145

mushrooms . . . utilize them . . . utilize them "as we go . . ."

C: What next?

S: . . . find some mushrooms . . . one very big one . . . big as my (expletive) head . . . not enough for attempt though . . . that's okay, Bill says he took the liberty of ordering five cases of farm grown mushrooms for the kitchen when I wasn't looking—as backup . . . says he stashed them in my back seat . . . I tell Bill I thought I'd made a mistake in ordering . . . he says no, it was just . . .

C: Okay, this is actually getting a little boring now. Let's skip ahead—what do you do next?

S: Walk . . . walk upstream as far as possible . . .

C: And then . . .

S: Try on pantie girdle and bra . . . try them on over my regular clothes of course . . . just sayin' . . .

C: And then . . .?

S: Bill dumps mushrooms in pantie-girdle open-spaces . . . stashes them in my other backseat, so to speak . . . then stuffs bra with mushrooms . . .

C: And then . . .?

S: Put PB&J sandwich in waterproof bag . . .

C: And then . . .?

S: Put on safety helmet . . .

C: Then what . . .?

S: It's getting hazy . . . my memory's getting very hazy . . .

C: Oh come on. You obviously floated the Firehole River. Any idiot could see that coming.

S: Oh yeah, I remember floating . . . floating the Firehole—on mushrooms. I now remember getting warm . . . (laughs) now remembering about boiling springs that empty into the Firehole river . . . getting warmer . . . smell of cooking mushrooms . . . mmmm, mushrooms . . .

C: What do you remember next?

S: Getting stuck . . . stuck in an eddy near a much hotter spring . . .

C: And then?

S: I remember sinking . . . sinking fast . . . but it's okay . . . I did it . . .!

C: So how do you feel now?

S: Great . . . but hungry . . . feel like taking a victory bite from my puffball & jelly sandwich . . .

C: Did you . . .?

S: No . . . handed it to a nearby fisherman instead . . . fisherman looked familiar . . . so familiar . . .

C: What do you remember now?

S: I remember walking . . . walking out of the Firehole River . . . to my car . . . walking and hoping . . . hoping mainly that no one sees me in my mushroom suit . . . or my mushroom helmet . . .

C: Do you remember anything else—anything at all?

S: I remember serving mushrooms later that day for lunch . . . slow-cooked mushrooms.

C: Okay, that's just about all I can take for one day—or forever really. When I count to three you'll snap out of the trance and unfortunately we'll both remember everything—one . . . two . . . *three.*

S: Wow! That was amazing.

C: No, that was disturbing. Now if you'll excuse me, I've got another client. He doesn't work for the general stores, but I'm doing this one for free—on my own time. And maybe I'm telling you too much already, but I don't care. He's a ranger, a ranger who, unlike *some* of my clients, is a brave and noble man. He's witnessed some horrific things, things seen while on drug stake-outs and the like.

S: Is his name *Smythe* by any chance?

C: How'd you . . . I mean, that's privileged informa . . .

And that's where the transcript ends.

Had it continued, though, it might have revealed that I drove straight back to Old Faithful Village by myself, leaving Bill "William Jennings" Bryan III (and I'm now sure that really *was* his name), to fend for himself.

But that part I remembered on my own. And I think I can safely assume that he was okay, that he eventually got a ride back to Idaho with the mysterious fly fisherman that I'd passed on the river, who I also assumed was one J. J. "Jim" Angleton II. I'll also assume that they both resumed their work there as consultants to the new movie, The Manchurian Candidate II.

And I wish now that I had one more opportunity to speak with my former "friend" and dish/brainwasher. Because if I did, I'd probably mention something to him about how the Salmon River, at least according to *my* research, tends to produce an even smaller yield of puffballs per acre along its banks than does the Firehole, and about that same river's *absolute lack of any hot springs whatsoever.* I might even go so far as to call into question the authenticity of his escape story altogether—and for what it's worth, ask what the point any of this was, if other than to merely obfuscate.

Furthermore, I might have asked him if it wasn't all part of a secret program, one designed to test out some sort of weapons-grade psychedelic on unsuspecting subjects.

And I would have asked Eva the same thing, had she not (mysteriously), packed up all her trusses and left before I got back—also never to be seen again.

But I did, of course, still see Ranger Smythe from time to time (meal time mainly), even though he no longer went near the sautéed mushrooms for some reason, and never had time for questions. I also saw the mysterious fly fisherman on occasion, and sometimes even saw he and Smythe together—in a rather curious and close proximity to each other. They were, however, both "anglophiles," so seeing them in the same fishing hole might just have been a coincidence.

Sometimes, though, you just have to wonder about life in general. And I usually do *my* wondering while out *wandering* in the field, pursuing my new hobby of toadstool painting. And you probably won't be too shocked to learn that I think about weird things when I'm out pursuing this new hobby, things like whether or not tiny little toadstools ever grow on tiny little toad stool-samples. And that's because I now paint most of my toadstools on mushrooms—the single most enjoyable way to paint anything.

Happiness is a Warm Carcass
(or Weekend at Bambi's)

As a longtime freelance nature photographer one of the questions I'm most frequently asked is: have you sold a picture yet? This then (as is always the case), will lead to a spirited debate and the inevitable follow-up question-of-semantics. But I should also mention (again), that I'm an equally longtime *anti-semantic*—a card-carrying one at that—so I'll usually just point out to Mom that "art is very subjective," and that "the day isn't over yet," before ending the call and fielding my next question.

And as "Resident Artist" at Old Faithful Lodge in Yellowstone National Park, I'll sometimes be able to *anticipate* a question and have it answered before it's even asked. This happens whenever a lost and confused-looking tourist wanders into the lobby and approaches my exhibit,

"We're in the Old Faithful *Lodge*," I'll explain. "You're probably looking for the Old Faithful *Inn* . . . the big historic building that you saw on the Travel Channel . . . the one that gets all the attention. If you go back out the same way you came in, and then take a right for about a quarter-mile you should be able to find it."

"Thanks . . ." lost tourist says before eventually becoming captivated by one or more of the many fine-art photographic prints I have on display. And that's when he usually alters his line of questioning, which I *don't* always preemptively answer,

". . . um, why do you have a picture of a dead baby deer on the wall? *Oh my God*, and there's a picture of a dead bear cub just below it!"

This particular question/comment is then typically followed by a moment of silence—silent irritation on my part. Why? Because the animals in question are *not* dead—or at least they weren't when I photographed them; they were merely lying down with their respective heads on the ground. And they're my only two pictures of baby animals that aren't either out of focus or blurred. So I refuse to take them down.

In fact it didn't even occur to me that they really did *look* dead until about the one-hundredth comment or question to that effect.

So I'll usually answer the once confused (now somewhat bemused), tourist by stating just that—that they're not dead,

". . . but if you're *into* that sort of thing, check out theses beauties over here on this wall. I call it my Carcass Collection. Or if you're more interested in *people* portraits," I'll continue, as I point to a "late-model" 14x24-inch glossy, "I shot this . . . uh, I mean I *photographed* this homeless guy on my recent trip to Bangkok. Looks real lifelike doesn't he?"

"I guess. But why did you pose him making an obscene gesture?"
Another moment of silence is then observed.

And it's just this kind of seemingly blatant misinterpretation that can make a less-grounded Resident Artist snap from all the irritation. *I*, however, will simply explain to the tourist that, "the model's hand is cupped like that—down by his groin—because he's begging for a handout," before repeating to myself that Van Gogh wasn't appreciated until after he was long gone either.

But how can a guy be irritated for long when it's springtime—springtime in Yellowstone. Baby bison are kicking up their heels; weekend photographers are down from Bozeman trying to capture said heels in mid-air (with their fancy digital cameras); and carcasses—winter-killed animals—half rotted and covered with maggots literally litter the land. And I usually avoid the crowds of photographers by finding a nice *out-of-the-way* carcass-filled meadow in which to do my thing.

Which begs the next obvious question: why do I photograph carcasses?

Because I *can!* Alright?

Outside of the fermentation process, *they* don't generally *move*. And when you're still working with a wide-angled 4x5 Crown Graphic view camera, that's important.

But it's not all about f-stops and apertures. There's the intricate logistics of it all to consider as well.

The typical carcass safari, for instance, starts long before sunup. After the caffeine kicks in around 4:30 am, you balance your camera-mounted tripod on your shoulder, stuff as many loaded sheet film holders (and a tube of toothpaste), into whatever coat pockets you have, and head out down the trail of your choosing—on an empty stomach. I can't stress the empty stomach part enough.

And a *dedicated* carcass hunter (a card-carrion one if you will), only *starts out* on the trail. You'll eventually want to veer *off* the trail, into the first dimly-illuminated meadow you see—or can see. Then, usually by the time your pant legs are fully saturated by the morning dew, you can get down to the business of squinting—squinting and squatting. The squatting gets you down low enough so that bones can be seen protruding from the tall grass. (It also serves to complete the trouser saturation process).

And the squinting part needs no explanation. If you're a professional photographer still using a Crown Graphic you're probably too cheap to buy binoculars.

So after squat-squinting for a few minutes, keeping in mind that ravens are more likely to be on the fresher bodies, you spot a potential subject. It looks like a bison. They're almost always bison. You then whip out your tube of Pepsodent, apply a dab under each nostril, and proceed to the body.

And as I say, that's the *typical* carcass hunt. The atypical one finds you setting up over a dead mule deer—who knows, maybe even the same one you photographed as a *live fawn* years ago.

But you're kind of disappointed because "Bambi" is pretty much all skin and bones, when you notice out of the corner of your eye a flock of ravens. They're on a much fresher carcass at the edge of the meadow. Turns out it's a big bull bison. And so you move the whole operation over there. And just as you're adjusting the camera bellows to get both of the bull's horns in focus, you notice coyote paw prints in the ground to your immediate right.

These would add interest to the photo you think, so you reposition. And just when you get the prints *and* both bison horns *all* in focus you notice bear prints behind where you just were—grizzly, judging by the length of the claws. And so you reposition once again. And just when you get re-repositioned and ready to expose the scene you notice a sound, a tranquility-shattering, tripod-vibrating, saturated-crotch-warming sound. It's from a bullhorn,

"Step away from the carcass! For your own protection, please step away!"

The ranger really doesn't have to tell you twice, you think.

Although there is perhaps a moment of hesitation—that one brief instant after having regained bladder control, and after seeing the real live grizzly returning to the carcass—when you actually *think* about refocusing on the bear.

But in the other, more prudent moments, you realize that refocusing probably isn't a viable option—with a view camera anyway. So you reposition once again—this time as instructed. And as you do so, *one hundred yards away from the carcass,* standing next to the ranger, his question to you: "are you out of your mind?" reminds you that you have to be back at your photo exhibit in the lobby by 10:00

am—to field other people's questions—questions that maybe aren't quite so harsh, or rhetorical,

"What's on that wall over there," a potential customer will ask after I'll have eventually made it back to my exhibit?

"Oh, that's my Carcass Collection," I'll reply, leading him over to the wall. "This one here is a real beaut—a mountain lion in case you couldn't tell. She used to purr like a kitten . . ."

Then "lost confused tourist" comes back into the lobby after having spent a few days heckling the *Inn's* Resident Artist, and waits patiently for me to finish my spiel.

"Have you shot any more 'live' subjects since I last talked with you?" he then asks, as any and all potential customers flee the scene.

"Day ain't over . . ." I'll respond, before continuing, ". . . but in order to really answer that question I'll first have to ask you to define the words *shoot* and . . ."

"You're a pro-semantic!" the tourist then blurts out excitedly.

And what if I am? This *is* America—America's first national park even—a place where a guy still has the right to change his position on such matters, if not the position of dead animals. What's more, he also has the right to field whichever questions he so chooses. And so if you'll excuse me, I think I hear my mother calling.

Making Book

Let's face it, way too much of this book is about me, me trying to "make it" in the pre-self-publishing days—what I like to call the Golden Age of Books. This chapter's no different. And if you've read even a handful of the other chapters in here you probably realize by now that I've had at least some success—getting three books published (all in the traditional sense), by a medium-sized publisher in a large western state.

But those were all photo books. Writing is another story altogether. It's much more difficult, for example, to get an editor to wade through a boring paragraph like this one, than it is to *show* the editor *photos*—compromising photos of him in a large western state. And ever since Mr. Merkle retired, taking his dignity (and his printing press), with him, I've had a much harder time getting published. It's a shame too, because I've written so much—so much of which will never be seen.

Mainly it won't be seen because those who would find it even the least bit interesting—can't see. They can't see fine print anyway. So I toyed with the idea of a collection of some of my older, more irrelevant pieces, coming out straight to large print—as "nostalgia"—and doing my book signings at various retirement homes. I nixed that notion right away. Much too depressing I thought—even for me. And it might be awkward were I to run into Old Man Merkle again.

One of those older pieces of mine questioned the absence of motel critics in newspapers and magazines. (Yes, you read that right—I said *motel* critics). These same newspapers and magazines, however, had no such shortage of restaurant, literature, and movie reviews. Today, of course, we lament the near absence of newspapers and magazines altogether—not to mention books.

That said, there *are* currently motel and hotel critics, it's just that they're all online—written by the actual hotel patrons themselves. And this actual patron was going to have his work on that topic seen—if only by future online hotel bookers. Who knows, maybe I'd even be "discovered"—by a big-time book publisher, one who might've possibly booked a sleazy hotel room in which to maybe possibly sneak around on his wife, his perfectly nice, medium-sized wife in a large eastern province, who we'll call, "Wang Ying."

This brings us back to my two main problems, one being that the places at which I've mostly stayed in the past weren't booked online, having gone out of business well before the advent of the internet. The other being that anymore I rarely stay at motels or hotels this side of the Ganges River. New research needed to be done. And so the following are examples of what one might find should he or she visit the average Asian-equivalent of Expedia or Travelocity, and read their reviews. The fact that they're published here—in book form— may or may not have anything to do with Wang Wei Publications (or Mr. Wang's spouse for that matter):

Shady Mangrove Beach Hotel and Resort
East Railay Bay, Krabi Provence, Thailand
The boat ride to West Railay, which is the only way to access East

Railay and the hotel, was very pleasant. The longtail boat's wake periodically sprayed my slightly sunburned face with cool saltwater and combined with the "boat-effect sea breeze" to make for ideal conditions. The boat then had to stop for one technical reason or another, most likely—as my boatman kept explaining, "Because of the dry land we bump into. You must get out now."

The *breezeless walk* from West Railay to East Railay met with *less* than ideal conditions. Somewhere along the way, though, a local "free agent luggage carrier" saw my sweat-soaked body and offered to help me to my hotel, presumably for some sort of gratuity.

RANDOM INTERJECTED TRAVEL TIP: When a local offers to carry your bags for you to your hotel—take him up on his offer!

Much later, during the last hundred yards or so to the hotel, where I again encountered the now-chuckling would-be free-agent bellman local who's offer I turned down, but who had also given me free directions to my hotel—the "scenic directions" it turns out—I spied a beautiful young Thai lady with a cool drink in her hand. This welcome to my hotel, I thought, might be just the remedy needed to help me forget my recent "scenic sojourn" through dense jungle, where at one point I may have had to detour around what appeared to be an ancient abandoned leopard snare, and where at another, I had to balance my two 50 lb. suitcases atop my head while wading through a body of water that various explorers at different points in history have labeled on their maps: Spider Lagoon, Scorpion Cove, and, Centipede Springs. Right now it's listed as Leech Lagoon.

And as I increasingly became aware that the drink being extended by the lovely young lady was really meant for the occupants of the yacht that had just pulled up and who were being carried one by one to the shore by imported Philippine boat boys, I let them pass, and trudged the five hundred additional yards to *my* hotel. The guys there, greeted me with a bow and the customary authentic Thai triage analysis, before putting me on their clinic's waiting list and showing me to my room—which, by the way, was nice, very nice in fact.

But before I could explore all the amenities of the room, I had to find the shower—the cold spray from which, I thought, might sooth my now throbbing third-degree sunburn. Also I figured I should wash the area on the back of my leg that had obviously been bitten or stung (at one very crucial point, I might add), during my balancing act in the lagoon.

And did I say the room was nice? Well, it was spacious too—as was the bathroom. In fact, one could have run wind sprints in the shower, had one's legs at the time not been the consistency of raw Thailandian rubber. But after a quick turn of the shower handle, I also found that one could walk outside and stand under one of the many stalactites in one of the many sea caves in the area, and get every bit as much water pressure. I, however, elected to walk out into the surf, where one could more fully experience the sting of salty seawater on various bites and abrasions while cleaning up.

The rest of my time at Shady Mangrove Beach Hotel and Resort was wonderful, even though I found out that it was one of those specialty resorts, and that the words "shady mangrove" were euphemistic. You see, Thailand is well known for being, "gay friendly." And whatever your thoughts on that specific subject (or shady mangroves in general), may be, you're no-doubt correct. But there are also probably fewer suicides by gay teenagers in Thailand per capita than anywhere else in the world. I applaud the Thai people for that. And not being gay, I managed to avoid any awkward confrontations the week I stayed there by simply declining all complementary massages, *nailing* the "do not disturb" sign on my door, and by being naturally unattractive.

I give Shady Mangrove Beach Hotel and Resort 7 out of 10 Thai Water Tortures.

Bertram Hotel

Lor 17 Geylang Ave., Aljunied, Singapore

Some places have a mini-fridge; some places *are* a mini-fridge

—without the benefit of cool temperatures. I opened the door to my room at the Bertram and instead of examining all the conveniences that lie within (as I usually do), I immediately looked for the door that would theoretically lead to the main room. The only door I found slid open (by necessity), and revealed a proportionally tiny bathroom. I then reached back into the main room with my left arm and pulled down the Murphy-style bed. This bed, a twin, completely filled the room—with the exception of a one-foot-wide strip of "living area" where my backpack and luggage lived for the duration.

But I didn't choose this place for its square footage, I chose it for its location. And after all, I've lived for months out of the back of my SUV—this place was luxurious by comparison.

Oh sure, I could have taken the quiet place in the adjacent district, the one located between the two rival Buddhist Meditation Centers and above Fragrant Bean-Curd Eating House. And my friends, Shawn and Lorraine, are always wanting me to stay with them, in their spacious, modern, mid-to-uptown, doorman salutin,' high falutin' high rise apartment complex. But no, I wanted to live in the "authentic Singapore," the one place in the city-state where they didn't all speak English, the only spot in a mostly spotless town where you could clear your throat in public and not get caned, the sole area in this, might-as-well-be-Utah, notoriously clean country that wasn't, if you'll pardon the platitude—sanitized for your protection.

And speaking of which, the Bertram Hotel's bathroom (as is typical of any Asian bathroom floor plan)—is laid out so as to enable a person to be able to perform all three "S" activities (if you know what I mean), without having to move an inch, *and* while in the (un-sanitized) seated position.

The Bertram Hotel as a whole is situated between Eating House #257 and Massage Parlor #189. It lies above Club Z Karaoke, and below Hokian Athletic Association PTE., LTD. At the rear of the building is a durian processing plant. And that's what ultimately downgraded the place for me.

Durians, if you don't know, are large spike-covered fruit that smell a little like the worst jungle-rotted foot in all of Southeast Asian military history—if that foot had been cut off and left to marinate in a large vat of lutefisk for several months. *Some* people like the taste. *No one* likes the smell.

The food at Eating House #257, however, is simply delicious—and cheap. So is the food at Eating House #256, #258, and so on and so on. The fruit at the many fruit stands in Singapore for some reason is more expensive than the prepared main dishes, but equally delicious.

And there's a nice little segregated fruit stand (they separate the durians from the good stuff), not far from the Bertram where I'd always like to go after a long day of walking from eating house to eating house. Hey, someone has to do it. And it became sort of a routine. My day's closing ritual, for example, would be to pay my quarter-equivalency for a quarter-pineapple, grab it in both hands like an ear of corn, and simply chomp away (to the distant karaoke beats of Glen Campbell or Neil Diamond), before eventually making my way through the maze of people, cars and bikes; past rusty restaurant fixtures, rusty shop gates, and moldy green underutilized trash bins. I'd sidestep cats, breath in the second-hand smoke, and peer over the myriad array of dirty Carlsberg Beer umbrella-stands to spot my hotel's entrance. I'd then climb up the two flights of stairs, unlock my door, and flop down on the flophouse bed for the night, falling asleep amid more 70s music and occasional loud yelps from the Thai Massage beat-down-recipients next door.

> RANDOM INTERJECTED TRAVEL TIP NO. 2: Be sure to thoroughly wipe the fruit juice and all other fruit residue from your face before going to sleep at the Bertram Hotel.

I'll then wake up the next morning to the sound of more loud yelps (from the Dojo above me), and think to myself that my morning chin stubble is a little on the thick side, not to mention—moving.

> RANDOM INTERJECTED TRAVEL TIP NO. 3: Make sure to pack extra single-blade disposable shavers, if you can't

adhere to the previous random interjected tip of wiping the fruit juice from your face.

I then go into my opening ritual of the day—that dealing with the three "S" activities, taking extra care to rinse the ants from my double blades during the shaving part.

I give the Bertram Hotel seven-and-a-half durians.

Bangkok Motor Court

Bangkok, Thailand

Most of the places at which I'd stayed in Thailand to this point had been fairly touristy. But, as in the case of Singapore, I wanted to experience the real Thailand—bugs and all. So when I booked this motel (and it really wasn't a *hotel*), I made sure it was off the beaten path, and that there was a certain "filth factor" involved. I was in luck too—or so I thought.

And as I waited at the "reception" desk for someone, *anyone* to show up, I noticed what appeared to be the motel's pest control strategy on top of the desk. These people certainly do things in an elegant way, I thought, as I further examined the open-air Thai-style wooden architecture and tiny furnishings that surrounded the trapped cockroach. I imagined the squiggly letters stamped on the outside of the structure as being translated to something like: "Roaches check in; but they don't check out *because there's no desk attendant anywhere*."

Then I heard a faint snoring sound and poked my head through the beads used for a door, woke the guy up, and eventually got my key. And as usual, even though it was late at night, I immediately inventoried all the room's amenities. A complementary condom on the pillow, was of course, the first sign I'd picked the right place. I, as usual, didn't (need to), use it. I then saw the room-service menu, with the actual picture of each lady next to her number and the services she provided. But next to that listing was another laminated sheet of paper that read: Please be advised that all room furnishings are the property of our motel. If you wish to purchase anything as a souvenir, please ask at "reception" (my quote marks) and we will be happy to sell you the following items: TV 5,000TBH; Refrigerator; 7,000TBH; Water Glass 50TBH; Bed Sheet 500TBH; Acrylic Blanket 1,200TBH; Towel 300TBH; Plastic Flowers w/Vase 400THB; Slippers 200TBH; Lamp 1,000TBH, Cockroach (with cage), *200,000TBH*—financing available. The last item is what threw me.

Like they *had* any cockroaches!

I looked everywhere for them. I even turned out the lights and suddenly turned them back on again as I quickly poked my head through the beads that served as my bathroom door. Nothing. But then again, it might have been easy to miss one due to the fact that the pattern on the bathroom wallpaper was in fact a cockroach pattern, a random cockroach pattern.

Whether this was: 1) by design, a tactic to make it easier to overlook the real one amid the fake armada; 2) a sign—that the motel manager had a sense of humor; or 3) pure reverence, I'll probably never know for sure. But I'm guessing the latter. In any case, the bathroom strobe-like light-and-pattern show made for some really interesting dreams—both that night, *and* the whole week.

Other features of the motel more or less contributing to those weird dreams included a 10-gallon-capacity pink-elephant-shaped water heater for the shower; a television that apparently got only a live feed of roosters fighting, real live roosters (outside the motel), the crowing of which you could hear night and day, but mostly day when there was less Bangkok noise to drown them out; a peep hole not-so-lovingly crafted by bullet; and *four* books in the nightstand drawer: The New Testament, The Teachings of Buddha, The Koran, and The Book of Mormon.

The dreams I had, by the way, were of me—participating in the weirdest Unitarian church service ever.

But after waking up the next day and eating breakfast (the non-complimentary bag of Thai Chi Toes ironically tasted less like feet than durian), I went to the "reception" desk to complain about the *TV* reception.

"You want to make book?" the "receptionist" (the only one I saw there all week), asked, still groggy from being awakened. "Bangkok is good place for making book."

"Not really," I said, nonplussed at his non sequitur, and wondering just how he knew I was a writer. "I'd rather *have* it published. But if I do end up making the book myself, I'll probably have it printed in the good old USA."

And despite the "receptionist's" very good English, there was quite a bit *more* confusion that day, not to mention that entire week.

RANDOM INTERJECTED TRAVEL TIP NO. 4: If you do end up buying a TV out of a Thailand motel, keep in mind that the real cost is in shipping it to the US. The same goes for Mitsubishi refrigerators.

The Bangkok Motor Hotel had only one housekeeper it seems too, an overworked guy, who apparently had a good sense of humor, always chortling whenever he saw me. One time when the housekeeper and I were together in the presence of the "receptionist" I asked the English-speaking "receptionist" what exactly was so funny.

"He say that we will save money on complimentary condoms with you here all week. Hahahahahaha!"

Wow! I didn't even know where to start with my response to that. Probably because I didn't even know how to say "thank you" in Thai. And then there was the potential problem of the likely confusion when explaining to them my situation with a girl in Singapore, my irrational preoccupation regarding a certain way-too-young-and-way-to-beautiful-for-me still-in-college violet-clad girl named "Pansy"—not to mention all the other reasons not to even accidentally support human trafficking.

RANDOM INTERJECTED TRAVEL TIP NO. 5: Accidentally-bought flowers (pansies or otherwise), are pretty reasonable to ship from Thailand to Singapore.

In the end, though, I kind of resented the fact that the "receptionist" never asked me to bet on the cockfights (given my past gambling problems—they could have made out big), and that there was only my one cockroach sighting (a caged one at that), despite all the dodgy-looking pictures of the place online. And although I do consider the establishment to be roach and rooster teases (wording it any other way might get this book banned in Utah and Singapore), I still give them five and-a-half (actual-sized), cockroach food dishes.

Hotel 96 Fragrance
Lor 19 Geylang Ave., Aljunied, Singapore

Back in the interesting part of Singapore and running low on funds I'd decided to stay in the absolute cheapest place there was. There are at least a dozen Hotel 96s in the Geylang district alone, so the franchise has had to add designations like "Fragrance," or "Lucky," or "Star," or "Cherry," to their names to differentiate them from one another. Mine (the Fragrance), was the least expensive of the bunch—and probably the sleaziest.

The place is located in the heart of the only real red light district in the country, and so in order to access the hotel (daytime or night), one must first pass by the working girls—one working girl every four-and-a-half feet. And if you've read my review of the Bangkok Motor Court (or are reading this in book form), you already know my stance on prostitution. It's nothing like the girl's stance—leaning casually against a lamppost, lit cigarette in hand. No, mine involves proper posture with my hands at my sides (feeling my pockets for my passport), and thinking up excuses as to why exactly I wouldn't be using the girl's services, which is really hard to do when that (usually beautiful), girl is simultaneously fondling your ego and your arm. Telling her the truth, I thought, might be somewhat inappropriate, as well as hard to get across. But most of the time she wouldn't understand very much English so I could *indicate* "no" and say just about anything to her proposition.

"We go your house for massage?" she might ask.

To which I'd respond (in broken English for some reason), "You very beautiful, but I want to be by myself for tonight."

To which she'd brokenheartedly responded by turning to the guy right behind me.

The hooker two girls down the block might then ask: "How about party at your place?"

"I have a girlfriend," I'd say.

To which she'd then respond, "You live at 'Fragrance,' you no have girlfriend."

I'd then pull away from her grasp and encounter another girl, and then another one, and then another.

A little trick I eventually learned would be to have some sort of "to go" container of food with me at all times so I could use that as an excuse not to partake. It also helped to keep the flies off the ever-swelling bite mark on the back of my leg. Of course in that part of Singapore "take-out" is easy to find. And it was on a somewhat older lady-of-the-evening that I first used this particular food ploy, pointing to my bag of pastry and apologetically explaining to her in my broken English:

"Butterfly buns . . . not getting any fresher."

And I've always wondered why I got such a dirty look from her, often speculating on the odds of whether or not she was in fact a "madam," and that her nickname would in fact be "Butterfly Buns," or that Madam Butterfly Buns would even know enough English to be insulted. I calculated they were about a thousand-to-one actually. And it's exactly ten-to-one odds that deep-fried butterfly buns will in fact take the place of sex for me some day. They're that good.

But my favorite excuse involving food which wasn't really an excuse, was my response to a very Americanized hooker who happened to question me about the contents of my cargo shorts.

"Yes, that is a banana in my pocket!" I said. "You saw me buy it . . . three seconds ago! In fact you had your hand in my other pocket at the time. Now I go home and eat my banana."

And upon reaching the lobby of the Hotel 96 Fragrance, I would more often than not be joined in the elevator by one of these same working girls—only she'd now be accompanied by a customer. Sometimes that customer would be what's known as a repeat customer. Sometimes that repeat customer will have what's known as a recognizable face, a very rich-looking recognizable face, the face perhaps of a "respected" pillar-of-the-community. Less often, however, would be the times I would get a knock at my hotel door (housekeeping at 96 Fragrance is pretty lax). But when I *would* get that knock and I *would* open the door expecting to get some fresh towels or linen, but instead got a distraught-looking wife, a perfectly nice, medium-sized wife from a large eastern province in China who has questions, I tend to stop and listen—especially when she's handing me an eight-by-ten glossy portrait, a portrait of a very recognizable rich-looking face.

And even though my date later that week with the lovely Pansy turned out to be more of a "living exhibit" at her university (who knew her Masters degree was in gerontology), I don't hold Hotel 96 Fragrance responsible for that, and therefore give them eight full butterfly buns.

You Peaked Mountain Resort & Spa (iffy English translation)
Zhangjiajie, Hunan Province, China

Jed Clampett and Mick "Crocodile" Dundee are two fictional characters who instantly come to mind as examples of someone who feels out of place in his fancy surroundings. Less obvious, but a better comparison to me, would be the character of John Buber (played by Andy Garcia), in the movie Heroes. I'm no hero, and I certainly don't look like Andy Garcia, but I have lived for periods of time in my vehicle like John Buber, who was suddenly thrust by dramatic and unforeseen circumstances, into incredibly extravagant accommodations—something to do with a plane crash. My circumstances were less dramatic—possibly having something to do with the blackmailing of an Asian businessman.

Plain and simple—You Peaked Mountain Resort is a palace.

Now, I don't normally use profane language, but a strange form of

Tourettes syndrome took over my vocal cords as I stepped out of the taxi in front of the hotel—Chinese cab rides can have that effect on you. I then did a quick inventory of all my body's organs—Chinese cab rides can have that effect on you.

> RANDOM INTERJECTED TRAVEL TIP No. 6: If at all possible arrange it so as to have a reputable transfer service pick you up at the airport, especially if that airport is more like a barn than an airport and there are a dozen-or-so ex-cons posing as taxi drivers waiting to fight over you and your voucher in order to give you a frenzied nighttime rally-race down city streets, up city streets, through long stretches of countryside, and back into the city (stopping periodically and inexplicably at what can only be described as clinics, dingy unsanitary-looking medical clinics), before reaching your destination—the hotel. Unless you want something like that.

The string of profanities continued to spew from my mouth as the uniformed bellman placed my belongings in my room and I entered.

"Bleep-bleeeep!" I said in awe of the place.

I then did my usual inventory of amenities, alternately inventorying—that night anyway—my recollections of the *cab ride* as well. Especially long "bleeps" came after 1) finding the three different shower nozzles located throughout the bathrooms (yes, I said bath-*rooms*—plural); 2) recalling during the cab ride the curbside pluck-ing of a chicken; 3) discovering the 42" wide TV recessed in the wall; 4) recalling the cab swerving through the over-the-shoulder basket toters trotting in double-time through the city streets; 5) the three, count 'em three telephones (one of them mounted next to the bidet); 6) recalling the cab driver driving past the "kids" who were "playing" with their Chinese throwing stars; and 7) the floor-to-ceil-ing mirrors everywhere, fun-house mirrors apparently.

This last feature of the You Peaked Mountain Resort made me

think that the hotel's name wasn't all that badly translated, because the ever-present mirrors showed me that I had in fact peaked—a long time ago—that peak never really being all that lofty in the first place. And I called them fun-house mirrors, until I realized that the only thing reflected in them that was disproportionate was me and my bao-like belly.

Don't get me wrong, I am extremely blessed, and I'm always well aware of that. We can't all be like Bruce Lee, and leave behind a beautiful corpse. But the You Peaked Mountain Resort, or more precisely the resort's surroundings, besides having an uncanny way of reminding me of my many blessings—also had a way of depressing me.

Every morning, for instance, I would avert my eyes as best I could from the fun-house mirrors, open my fancy curtains, and peer past the peasants to the clouds of pollution hiding the mountains beyond. I was supposed to be photographing those mountains. But where were they? So my first week there was spent looking for any sign of the sun—*and* an English-speaking guide. And every morning I would routinely ask the doorman to lower the drawbridge so I could walk through the peasants in search of a travel agency. Some of these people—who I only facetiously call peasants—were known (by me at least), as the: Strawberry Pyramid People.

There were about six or seven of them lined up in a row, sitting in the cold gray polluted air, under his or her own individual cold gray umbrella stand. And each had a one-foot-tall pyramid of cold gray strawberries on a plate. Thinking back, I didn't see any other strawberries anywhere. None whatsoever. There was a car parked behind them, but the trunk was open and I could see that it was empty. No bags, no baskets, no anything. Nothing that would indicate backup berries anyway. So I could only imagine that if one of them sold his or her pyramid that day, he or she'd spend the next day picking more strawberries before then constructing another pyramid. Amway it wasn't. But it *was* like this every single day. It didn't seem like much of a life.

And even without these sights it only takes me about a couple weeks in a sunless world to start feeling the effects of SAD (Seasonal Affective Disorder). The first signs of the bird flu, however, are noticed much more quickly.

> RANDOM INTERJECTED TRAVEL TIP NO. 7: If you have to get deathly ill in China, missing probably your only chance to get a decent landscape photograph in that country— get deathly ill in a hotel as luxurious as this one.

But this year I started feeling the effects of the flu only after my first full week there. And so I spent the next week in bed, with every wonderful member of the hotel staff attending to my needs and force feeding me every known Chinese home remedy available. And it was only after I began to actually believe I would live to see another day, that I started really thinking about my situation, getting philosophical even.

I recalled a story by Voltaire that some college professor forced me to read. The protagonist of the story, Candide, after all his adventurous travels, his ups and downs, his victories and defeats, finally came to the conclusion that going home, tending to the soil and growing his crops was all there really was to life. And that that life could be pretty darn good.

Holy bleep that was one long bleeping story! Kind of like this one. And I occasionally find myself cussing out that bleeping professor under my breath for making me read the whole bleeping thing.

But I vowed that if I ever got back home (and why wouldn't I?), to be the Strawberry Pyramid Person of Yellowstone National Park. I would simply help the tourists there find the geyser, find the waterfall, find the bathrooms, and maybe—somewhere down the line— find *this* chapter, in *this* book.

The proverbial dollar signs then lit up my eyes as I started to feel much better and the Chinese hallucinogens wore off. The bite mark on the back of my leg even started to go away. I then went outside for the first time in a week and a person selling strawberries on the street corner who noticed my camera pointed out a travel service that specialized in helping people like me get area mountain photography. The pollution and seasonal affective disorder lifted for a couple of hours and I got a few decent photos—not to mention *a lot* of perspective.

I give You Peaked Mountain Resort and Spa one big Chinese throwing star.

Radio Flier

My friend Paul—of the Fathead nation—was always sharing his rich tribal heritage. In fact, not long after we first met he shared a rich tribal legend about the origins of his people.

It told of an underground radio station that existed somewhere in the heart of Central California's garlic country, an underground radio station where time flew like arrows. Not all that interesting really. But Paul went on to explain that that very same "time" at that very same "station," still flies like arrows, but that fruit flies like bananas. Okay, that made it only slightly more interesting. But I guess they said things like that on the air—corny things. They made up for it, however, by playing good music. It was KFAT—94.5 FM, "the wide spot on the dial,"—or just K-Fat radio. And anyone who listened *religiously* became a Fathead medicine man.

Now some say that Paul looked almost exactly like G. Gordon (He-Who-Sent-Leary-Up-For-Less-Than-A-Lid) Liddy, of the Crazy Son of a Bitch tribe. So I exercised great caution whenever Paul spoke of the "Free Mexican Airline" song that K-Fat used to play, or when he actually offered me some "medicine" from his ceremonial peace pipe. You never know when you're going to be set up (by the Crazy Sons of Bitches). And you have to be especially careful when in a *federal* jurisdiction. Then one day I happened to pick up a *live* G. Gordon radio broadcast *while in Paul's presence*, after which the Free Mexican Airline was free to fly. But being naturally paranoid (paranoid on life you might say), I still wouldn't board. I wouldn't even get near long term parking. I couldn't afford to lose my job. This, of course, prompted Paul and his fellow tribesmen to give me the honorary Fathead name of: He-Who-Walks-With-Wooden-Rectum.

And the job I couldn't afford to lose was that of cook—a cook cooking three meals a day, seven days a week, for a small group of Old Faithful Village employees, one of whom being Paul. And I know. It's really sad that I needed that particular job. But Paul was equally sad. He *voluntarily* got up as early as I did, only for no other apparent reasons than to watch me prep breakfast; make suggestions for upcoming meals; and—as I mentioned earlier—offer insights into his heritage. The man could really chew the K-Fat.

And he couldn't help but notice my own affinity for the AM air wave, and even thought that I possessed some sort of special C.I.A. radio (the mutual suspicion, I might add, was quite high there for awhile). He said he'd never seen anyone who could pick up such distant stations seemingly at will. And every station's distant when you're in Yellowstone. But it wasn't the radio, it was the hours I— we kept. I guess Paul didn't know, despite *his* not having much of a life either, that radio signals come in stronger and clearer during times of darkness, and that crazy people—if they really "channel" their angst—can pull in stations better than sane ones. It has something to do with electrolytic imbalances in the brain.

And as I held my one bare hand over the stove's pilot light one morning, and the other on a radio's antenna, Paul asked me who I was listening to.

"Oh, just some lunatic right-wing wacko," I said, my electrolytes leaning a little to the left that morning. "He's coming in real clear though—right now he's describing how it's possible to *kill* someone with a *grapefruit knife*."

"It's too bad K-Fat's not broadcasting anymore," Paul said. "They're a little wacko to the other extreme." He then sighed as he watched me snap a wooden spoon off in the oatmeal before adding, "I sure do miss those Fat Fries they held."

Then, after a new K-Fat spiel, Paul began his daily suggestion ritual—a "Fat Fry" being the natural addition that day to his usual artichoke suggestion ("the majority of which are grown by a neighboring 'tribe' in California"), not to mention more fresh garlic in everything. But Paul wasn't the only one. *All* the employees suggested things, from goat cheese to chokecherries. Now where, I thought to myself, would I get exotic ingredients like those at Old Faithful Village? They only import the good stuff for high-paying tourists at the Inn.

"Will these be enough," a voice then rang out, as I turned—instinctively wielding a weapon?

I found Paul standing below me, holding a produce crate full of artichokes.

"You know," I answered while perched atop a prep table in the classic Ninja pose, "you should never sneak up behind someone when they're gutting a grapefruit. I could've killed you."

And the Fatheads are indeed a stealthy bunch. I hadn't even noticed that Paul had *left*, let alone come back from his van with bounty. The same was true, I presumed (only in reverse order), with regard to his artichoke-growing neighbors in California—we'll call them the Castrovilleheads—who a week after the fact were no-doubt only now missing some of their inventory.

"I'm willing to donate these," Paul then said. "All you have to do is husk them. And that grapefruit knife you're waving at me might be just the thing for that too."

And so unfortunately without the ingredient excuse anymore, I agreed to his artichoke-themed Fat Fry. My only stipulation, as in a story first told by U. Utah Phillips on K-Fat radio, a story called "Moose Turd Pie," and re-told to me by Paul, was that the first person who complained about the food at the Fat Fry had to take over cooking for me, at least for a day. That way I'd have some time off to actually enjoy the park, maybe even walk around a geyser basin— Biscuit Basin for example.

And the next day as we found ourselves with *way too much time off* (a suspension without pay), walking around that very basin, and thinking up hypothetical names for the new hypothetical underground radio station I'd proposed for the area, Paul (the sulfur fumes clearly inspiring him), chimed in.

"How about 'K-Fart radio?'"

"No," I told him. "I was thinking more along the lines of: 'Air Biscuit.'"

"And what kind of things would you broadcast?" he asked.

"Funny you should ask," I responded coldly.

I then launched into an entire monologue of the events leading up to our *"freedom walk"*—using *my special version* of U. Utah Phillips' legendary piece, which went a little something like this:

> I'll tell you about the worst job I ever had. It was cooking for a bunch of thankless savages right here in Yellowstone National Park. That's what they used to call employees here—savages. And so I guess that made me one too. Anyway, I'd managed to convince these ingrates who I cooked for, which included a "plumber/burglar" named Paul, to go along with a stipulation. And this stipulation to which they agreed was that the first person who complained about the cooking had to become the cook for a day.
>
> So, armed with that proviso, I sallied forth into the back of the walk-in refrigerator and spied a bunch of over-ripe donated artichokes. After pivoting to my left,

my eyes fell on some sort of weird cherries—also donated, and fairly overripe. Inspiration then hit me and
I said to myself, "Self, you're going to bake up a big
ol' artichokecherry pie." Because if anybody complained
about my cooking, *they* were going to have to cook.

So I got my stuff together—in the "Moose Turd" version, though, they said something other than *stuff*—and
proceeded to the prep table. I took one "stab" at cleaning
the artichokes, and then threw away the grapefruit knife.
If something ever had to be done Fathead-style it was
this. Real Fatheads, you see, didn't waste any part of the
artichoke. And the kitchen I worked in just happened to
have one of those heavy-duty Buffalo Chopper food processors that made quick work of the strange vegetable,
turning it into a thick puree that when combined with
berries, fresh Gilroy garlic, and a half-cup of corn starch,
was just perfect for pie filling.

I then rolled out a couple of beautiful pie shells, putting them in pans just as slick as you please. I crimped
them with my thumbs, and laid strips of dough over the
filling and garnished it with some kind of herb that that
Paul fellow also donated. It came out beautiful; poetry on
a plate—ifin', of course, the poet was named Poe. And
then I served it up for desert, waiting for the first hint of a
complaint. Well, that Paul guy comes over, see—throws
hisself down like a fool on a stool. Picked up his fork.
Took a big ol' bite of that pie. Then he threw down his
fork, gagged a little, choked some, then gagged a lot, and
finally yelled,

"My God! That's Artichokecherry pie . . . it's good
though."

That's basically where the corresponding part of the *U. Utah
Phillips story* ends. *My* story, however—to be aired (in an alternate
universe), on Air Biscuit Radio—continued with a surprise health

inspection, and ended with the protagonist (Y. Yellowstone Pete), having more time off to walk around geyser basins than he actually wanted. Hence this "freedom walk without pay."

"Looking back," Paul asked as we eventually reached Emeril Spring, "don't you think you really should have waited until after you baked the pie to garnish it? I mean you being a lightweight and all."

And bam! That's when it hit me—the contact-high aspect of the story that is (and/or the fact that when you're stoned everything purportedly tastes good). It might have even been a delayed reaction of sorts.

"You're right," I answered as we stared down at a bunch of brine flies in Emeril Spring's runoff channel. "But you know what they'll say on Air Biscuit Radio? They'll say: 'Time flies like arrows; but brine flies like bacteria.'"

"I guess a billion brine flies *can* be wrong," Paul then said, holding his nose. "It's too bad health inspectors aren't the same way. What are you going to call your next imaginary radio station—that is, now that you have only 24 hours to leave the park."

"I don't know," I said, my electrolytes leaning a little to the right and depressed about having to take a leave of absence. "Savage Vacation comes to mind."

Ah, but even He-Who-Walks-With-Wooden-Rectum wasn't that disturbed.

Pinocchio Rose
and the War on Nose Candy

Yeah, yeah, I heard 'em all—all the juvenile sayings directed my way, all the insulting clichés. And so I even made one up myself—owned it, so to speak. At least *my* saying would be original, albeit a variation on another old quote:

> When God was handing out noses, I thought she
> said *hoses* and so I said, "give me fifty feet of red."

Okay, it's not all that funny—but I was only fourteen years-old at the time. Give me a break.

And so you can see how I turned out the way I did, especially after getting the nickname "Pinocchio Rose"—in ninth-grade history class. (Yes, my classmates all had small noses *and* better comedic sensibilities, which made it hurt all the more).

And how did I turn out you ask? I turned out a rosy-nosed hose-head with a distrust of people, spreading propaganda (or attempting

176

to anyway), in the Pacific Theatre—not to mention a person who would seriously consider the offer made to him of sharing some sort of illicit drug (or two), with a man simply named M.

Now I don't know if there's a war on drugs in Thailand like there is in the US, or if there's ever been a movie house *named*, "The Pacific Theatre," but there shouldn't be, and there should—respectively.

That's my propaganda. Short, to the point—and still relatively unfunny.

But the story's not over. Not even close. You see, being an old man—an obscure old man at that—who's only goal left in life was to become a published author, my best shot at getting any kind of exposure at the time appeared to *be* to rent a plane and do some pamphleteering over Phang Nga Bay. (If there *were* anti-littering laws in Thailand they didn't appear to be regularly enforced).

Phang Nga Bay is in Southern Thailand, which some historians, mainly the ones I found on Wikipedia, consider to have been a part of the Pacific Theatre during WWII. Okay, it's a stretch, but there was *some* fighting in nearby Laos, and since I didn't write my propaganda in Laos, and I needed to tie the whole Pinocchio Rose-Pacific Theatre pamphleteering thing to Thailand (for this story), I looked up poetic license in my bookmarked Strunk & White online manual of style—and then Google-mapped the nearest Kinkos—before becoming extremely depressed.

In all the searching, though, I did find that plastic surgery in Thailand was less expensive than, say for instance, even a *five-minute* jaunt over Phang Nga Bay in a chartered WWI era bi-plane. The depression then returned as I learned the kind of plastic surgery in which the medical establishment in question specialized, had more to do with Thai "ladyboys" and lavish cabarets than reductions in the length of a person's nose.

I sighed, thinking that unless you're a celebrity or have already led an amazingly interesting life, like William S. Burroughs or Siam Lightner, and have at least a *somewhat* talented ghost-writer with an agent who knows a plastic surgeon, you don't have a ghost of a chance at getting your writing published—or nose reduced for that matter. You can't just be a good writer anymore.

Furthermore, just being an American living in Thailand, especially one living at a place offering high speed internet, doesn't automatically qualify you as having led even a semi-interesting life.

More unfunny propaganda? Maybe.

But that's still not the end of the story.

Not when there's a James Bond-like character named M in it to potentially spice things up—and an actual island in Phang Nga bay *called* James Bond Island. The island's original name, of course, was something like Koh Tapu and probably means something like "enormous Gatorade bottle balanced upside-down on the surface of the water" because that's what it looked like.

I qualify these and future statements with, "something likes" and "I thinks," because at the time of writing this particular paragraph the hotel's internet connection inexplicably went out, and I couldn't fact-check or research anything. Come to think of it, that's about when the air-conditioner began to steadily emit less and less cool air, but when I, coincidentally, started to feel more and more like a real honest-to-goodness dues-paying writer.

Koh Tapu was where one of the James Bond movies was filmed (I think Man with the Golden Gun—*I'm not sure!*), and the obvious reason for its current name of James Bond Island. Far from the only interesting feature in Southern Thailand, this part of the world boasts of fantastically formed limestone islands, overhanging stalactite-covered cliffs, and towering ocean spires the way Minnesota boasts of lakes (only with 40% *more* humidity). Here you'll find mountainous maritime marital aids—if Dr. Seuss designed marital aids—rising dramatically from the Andaman Sea. You half-expect King Kong to emerge from one of the enormous sea cliff caves fleeing from an evil Ian Fleming villain. Not lost in all this is that this incredibly bizarre archipelago is also a vast jungle gym for rock jocks.

And turns out—that's all M was.

One of the many rock climbing guides in the area loosely affiliated with one of the many rock climbing shops, M just happened to be loosely tied that day to a shop with the unusual name (for Thailand anyway), of Tex Climbing Guides—which as you'll later find out, ends up being somewhat apropos.

But I didn't meet M at the shop. I met him on one of the trails leading to a climbing area. These "approaches" as such trails are called, are often more adventurous than the actual climbs. Fixed ropes— long since retired (and donated by climbing guides perhaps)—aid you (and your heavy backpack), up, over, and across steep muddy inclines, bottomless chasms, and protrusions of what's known as "dagger rock" to the base of the climb itself.

And M, while not exactly a typical guide (he didn't have dreadlocks or a funky knit hat), did adopt the perfunctory Bahamian accent to go along with his broken English, and wore a pretty cool Bob Marley tee-shirt—at least the first time I saw him. But since he didn't have on this "full uniform" I didn't know he was a guide. And the second time I saw him I'd just searched him out because of his offer, an offer I hoped could help me experience at least a little more of an amazingly interesting life, a la William S. Burroughs, or Siam (call me Sam) Lightner, but mainly like William S. Burroughs—the junkie. In my case I'd settle for being just a snow blower, or stoner— if only for a day.

So imagine my disappointment when M led me to the climbing area known as Nose Candy Cave and whipped not from his jock a rock of cocaine, but from his bag—a block of chalk.

Chalk, I should point out to those who don't know, is applied to a climber's hands in order to absorb sweat—one of Thailand's most plentiful naturally-occurring renewable resources. Neither, however, is a substance to be snorted.

"We're going to need a lot of this, if we are to do Nose-Candy Cane," M said, pointing out a large cane-shaped stalactite extending out from the roof of Nose Candy Cave and curving down toward the ocean.

"But the scary part is over," M half-jokingly continued, referring to the approach. "Now we tie into new rope, and clip into fresh bolts."

"Shark!" a loud voice then rang out from above us.

This not-so-dulcet declaration of sea life, as I learned later, just so happened to have come from one Sam (Please Stop calling Me Siam) Lightner. It was yet another of those happy little coincidences that seem to follow me around. But I didn't recognize Sam at the time— probably because I'd never met him before and didn't know what he looked like. He was always just a name listed in a climbing guide-book—although listed next to some incredibly difficult first ascents. Sam, you see, is well-known among climbers for his intrepid exploits in the kingdom of Siam, or as it's better known today—Thailand.

I, however, was well-*un*known for my extrepid *in*ploits . . . behind word processors . . . in cushy hotel rooms. But if I am to ever be known for anything, ironically, it'll be for my uncanny brushes with fame, and my dropping of said names. So at the time, after hearing someone shout out "Shark!" from above (on a route named Thai Stick by the way), I naturally and reflexively thought that that person (who, of course, turned out to be Sam), had dropped a piece of gear or dislodged a chunk of limestone and was yelling out "Rock!" to warn us to take cover. And as is pointed out in another of my virtually unread stories (Big Rock Candy Chickenheads), the name to shout out after you *drop* a *name*—(while either out on the crags cragging or simply *writing* about being out on the crags cragging)—is of course: "Craig!" It's only polite.

But sometimes you can be too clever for your own good. And so after I came out from under the cover of the cave, and witnessed the tail end of the four foot-tall rooster tail wake kicked up by a couple of people snorkeling in the ocean three hundred vertical meters directly below us, and M explained that, "there is no rock falling, that was just my friend Sam Lightner yelling out 'Shark!' to be funny," I tried to explain my tongue-in-cheek version of name-dropping etiquette to someone who spoke rudimentary English . . . as a fourth language.

"Why should I yell out 'Craig,'" M asked?

"Never mind," I said, it's not important. "Belay on."

"Climbing," he countered, his bewildered look turning into a look of concentration.

"Climb on," I replied.

And did he ever. A symphony on stone with graceful, efficient movements (in D minor), M seemed at peace with the rock.

When he was finished, I lowered him back down to the base of the climb, which, by the way, was practically a hanging belay—hanging three hundred meters above the now-*almost*-calm snorkel wake.

Now it was my turn to climb that same climb.

And did I ever . . . suck. A cacophony on calcium carbonate with *un*graceful, *in*efficient movements (in F minor), I waged an *un*holy war on Nose Candy Cane.

Anguished cries from me, and the constant shouts of encouragement and coaching from other now-interested on-looking climbers: "put your left hand where your right foot was," "ya mon, good," "layback on that side-pull," "yes, yes" "stem out more," "good job," "heel hook that overhang," "no, no, nasal hook that 'chickenhead,'" all combined with the jack-hammering AK47-esque noise and rock dust stirred up by Sam Lightner's masonry drill to make for a scene reminiscent of the infamous Combat/F-Troop crossover episode of October 1962.

Aside from all that, it's important to note that "leading" is the difficult more dangerous aspect of climbing, which is what M did, allowing me the luxury of simply top-roping the same climb—a much, much easier task, although an impossible one for me that day.

Upon reaching the midpoint of the climb I was drained physically, about as drained as a person can get—but far from spent emotionally.

And as I came down off that incredible high, Sam (Siam I Am . . . Not), Lightner, also was being lowered. We reached M at about the same time, and before even untying, Sam dropped his glue-gun and drill and put his arm around my belayer.

"How have you been Soley," Sam asked, I haven't seen you in ages.

"Soley?" I thought, as they conversed—warmly—the way friends who have seen many adventures together often do.

And being an aspiring writer, I, of course, took as many mental notes of the conversation as was possible, at least as was possible for a person whose quivering jellyfish body lay conforming to an outcrop of the aforementioned aptly-named dagger rock.

Sam then noticed my morphing mass of goo and casually asked, "So who are you working for today Soley?"

And by that he wasn't referring to me, he meant, what rock climbing shop was he working for?

M, or should I say *Soley*, put a finger to his lips and said, "Shhh, today I am not Soley. Today I am M." And then to Sam's quizzical look, he explained, "If people heard that Soley gave away free rides on Nose Candy Cane, everyone would want one."

They then both gave a knowing laugh before Soley began directing his words to me, "Yes, this one's free," he said, "but the next one's going to cost you."

And I was indeed hooked—not so much on climbing, I'd been an off again on again enthusiast of the sport my entire adult life—but I was hooked on Soley (which, incidentally, rhymes with belay—a bit of climbing (and sailing), jargon meaning: to hold fast. In this case with ropes).

And he held me fast on many climbs throughout the next few months as I got into better climbing shape. But more than just a physical trainer, Soley, who *had* soul, also had an uncanny way of training someone else's.

I worked professionally as a photographer at the time—not as a writer—and Soley helped me to realize that my best bet to accomplish whatever future goals I might have was, in essence, to not *have* any, but to find the purpose in whatever you're *doing* in the moment. His words, paraphrased, were: if you are truly "enjoying," the handhold right in front of you, you won't care if you reach the top of the climb—but chances are you eventually will.

This triggered in my memory a saying I learned in a high school composition class: if you don't enjoy *writing* a story; no one will enjoy *reading* it.

And so as a bead of sweat finished its long journey from my forehead to drip off the end of my nose—onto my keyboard, I looked up from that keyboard to see some sort of small lizard (*I can't tell you what kind exactly!*), making its way—one "handhold" at a time across the wall. And that's when I realized I couldn't help but enjoy writing about Soley.

Sam Lightner (to continue my tradition of name-dropping), once made it a point to look me in the eye and state that "there are many Thai climbing guides, but Soley is one of the few Thai *climbers*."

I understood the distinction.

Soley Onbut was listed right along-side of Sam and other Western climbers such as Todd Skinner and Chris Sharma as having put up extremely difficult routes. And he voluntarily helped "Mr. Sam" and others associated with the Titanium Project (an enormous undertaking to replace all the unsafe stainless steel and aluminum expansion bolts with more durable titanium ones), just to make climbing in Thailand safer for others. But (like Sam), he didn't seem to care about getting any recognition for his efforts.

So when Soley also volunteered a good portion of his off time to show me some of the more picturesque areas around Krabi for me to photograph—and even relented to posing for some of the climbing pictures, I felt incredibly honored.

But one thing stood out about our discussions regarding the pictures I would take of him. I could take all I wanted, but under no circumstance was I to show any to him. He grimaced and shook his head at the thought.

I was dumbfounded.

Could this bronze Thai god, this picturesque "Limestone Cowboy of the Far East" (have rope will travel), this person who faced getting killed every day, inadvertently but ironically at the hands of people who paid him, this wise sage, the coolest guy on the planet—my hero . . . could this person actually be self-conscious?

It was, of course, completely insane . . . but, well it made me feel a little better about myself.

And in a larger sense, everyone with whom I seemed to come in contact in Thailand had at least some of Soley's qualities, from a boatman to the person preparing my peanut butter/banana/mango Thai pancake. Their outlooks were amazing despite having a much harder life than most Westerners—and *really* amazing in light of some outright hardships.

Take my regular Taxi driver Yao for example. His first wife died in a motorbike accident. His second one barely survived a similar collision and needs medicine they really can't afford. At some point after that, Yao adopted a baby boy and still gets misty-eyed whenever talking about him and the horrible conditions in which he found little Jo Jo. Sure, a baht sign does light up in Yao's eyes whenever he sees me coming, but that's understandable, and not (as I cynically assumed at first), the reason he wouldn't recommend a good motorbike rental place.

Soley was washed out to sea during the Tsunami of 2004 (*or whenever it happened!*). He barely survived—and I'm guessing he had to rebuild his entire life, as well as his shattered leg. I say I'm guessing because I didn't want to "go there" after sensing some sadness in his expression. Both he *and* Yao went out of their way help me get photos of his beautiful country—yes, for the money, but also because they could see I really needed help, a vision for which you needn't exactly seek out a qualified psychic. But I've also been accused by each of being "a good man," which embarrassed me greatly, but also motivated me to live up to their compliment.

And so it made me feel kind of silly dwelling on insults and juvenile comments made over thirty years ago. It spurred me forward, to *understand* the situation instead of continuing to react negatively to it. Maybe it was a matter of overcompensation—*on their part*—based on their own insecurities. And so to those boys coming of age in ninth-grade history class (not to mention *showering* after the next period's gym class), I only have this to say:

When God was handing out "hoses" you must have thought she said *noses* and asked for the smallest one they had.

And that's my propaganda—funny or not.

Cabin Fervor:
One Girl and a Sippy-Cup

S ometimes I long for my cabin—mainly during the Yellowstone
off-season—when I don't have access to it. And sometimes I
even long for the Pedophiliamobile, a pockmarked (from hail), '97
Chrysler mini-van, that at one time—pre-cabin days—served a purpose. No—not *that* purpose! I'm not a pedophile—(despite what you
may think about single males who drive minivans). That's just the
self-deprecating, appearances-can-be-deceiving, *nickname* I gave to
the van.

And I'm not referring to the van's purpose as a means of transportation either, a way to get me from lookout point "A" to lookout
point "B" for early morning photo shoots.

No, I'm talking about the vehicle's actual designation as a mini-
van, a rather nice looking mini-van, which served the purpose of
blending in with all the other nice-looking parked vehicles, to perhaps make it look as if its owner (me), was a family man, someone

a ranger, for instance, might not suspect would be sleeping in it . . . somewhat illegally . . . in various hotel parking lots throughout the greater Yellowstone region.

I had it "customized" for that purpose too. An infant car seat was strapped to the front passenger seat, and a Tommy Tippy brand sippy-cup filled with loose change sat on the dash in plain sight of rangers' flashlight beams. The quarters in the sippy-cup, incidentally, were the only denomination incapable (upon shaking), of making it through the cup's nickel-sized mouth slot, thus automatically saving them for Laundromats (a stroke of genius if I do say so myself). I even found a doll to fit in the car seat for those times when I had to *drive* by a ranger station on the way to one of the various parking lots, and needed to "sell" my family image all the more.

Somewhere along the way, though, the mini-van got less respectable-looking, due in part to time, but mainly due to some tennis ball-sized hail-related "incidenting"—(or as the Dent Doctors of Psychology like to call it—imprinting). Talk about trauma. But that's another story altogether, and in the end, it really didn't matter—I landed a position in Yellowstone whereby I had full use of a cabin for the summer season. No more sleeping around in parking lots just to avoid costly campgrounds.

So as I sat, one *off*-season, in the drivers-side seat of my *current* vehicle, the "Wheeled Womb," watching storm clouds gathering on the horizon and longing for the cabin—I once again reflected on an incident. It was a non-hail-related incident, but equally traumatic:

At the time, I still had the Pedophiliamobile, complete with accoutrement (hey, the "change holder" still served a purpose), but I was no longer the van's full-time resident—I had my cabin in which to sleep. It was summertime in Yellowstone, I was Resident Photographer at Old Faithful Village and all was right with the world. And with this newfound status, I soon discovered that despite *me* and my *van's* relatively decrepit conditions I could still occasionally turn the head of a young lady or two. No, not those of *American* young ladies—but those heads belonging to young ladies who were a part of what I like to call the Asian Invasion of Yellowstone Nation.

The invasion began in the late eighties, or early nineties when National Park concessionaires started recruiting summer workers from overseas. They came from all *over* the world, but mostly from the countries of Singapore, China, and Taiwan. Some of them worked in retail, where he or she sold knickknacks that came mostly from Singapore, China, and Taiwan. Others worked in housekeeping, while still others worked in food service. Many Americans complained about this invasion, but I for one welcomed it—if only for selfish reasons.

You see, there's a part of modern Asian culture that holds in very high esteem the art of photography and those who practice it. They even have what's known as, "Focus Groupies," those who would travel far and wide just to worship at the feet of a master practitioner. (Okay, "Focus Groupies," is just my made-up name for the sect, but I did test the name out on hundreds of people before trademarking it). And, of course, we all know that young Asian women are almost always attracted to older Caucasian men—be they a photographer or not.

Or it could be that the above "information" is only an opinion, an ugly-American belief, based on what's commonly known by *non*-delusional people as—wishful thinking.

Still, I may have held one or both of those beliefs at a certain point in my life. And as I stepped outside my cabin early one morning to soak in the wonderland sun, scratch my gelatinous mid-section, and clear from my lungs in one loud "hork" the previous night's accumulation of liquefied pine pollen (Yellowstone gold), one of those heads turned in my direction.

"Oh my God! Are you alright?" the backlit vision-in-white asked.

And was I ever. But I still had to quickly reenter my cabin. One doesn't properly answer an apparition's questions without pants. And as I poked my head back out the door to see if what I thought I saw was real, I realized that it, or rather she, was. Not only was she real, she was now crouched over my small Coleman grill, examining it with no small amount of reverence.

"Hawn-how," I said, making the assumption that she was Chinese and trying to answer her question.

She looked up at me quizzically, waiting for an explanation.

"Oh, I'm sorry, you must not speak Mandarin," I said.

"Of course I speak Mandarin," she countered. "I'm from China. But what were *you* speaking?"

Things then got even more confusing as she tried to teach me the proper way to pronounce *hawn-how* and then asked for directions to Mawrraud Rake. She was on her way to whatever that was.

Ten minutes later, at an oratorical impasse, she changed the subject.

"They let you cook here?" she asked, referring to the small row of employee cabins and my charcoal grill. "We can't cook where I live in the dormitory, we have to eat in the employee dining room. It's horrible, horrible food!"

She then glanced through the open door of my cabin. "And you have a refrigerator?" she continued. "Any chance you might have a wok?"

"I know of a nice walk," I answered, it's about two miles, and ends at Mallard Lake. I'll take you there. Just give me a few seconds to round up my, uh, *professional* camera gear."

"Do you think we can get some fresh duck meat at Mawrraud Rake," she then asked?

And despite her love of good food, Angel—which was her American first name (I never could pronounce her Chinese one)—was very slim and trim. And despite her complete *indifference* to all things *photography related*, she wasn't entirely repulsed by me. There were even moments of delusional bliss when I actually thought she was attracted. And I of course liked any beautiful female who would give me the time of day. So, naturally, I jumped at the chance when Angel offered to cook an authentic Chinese meal for me at my cabin.

Problem was, my cabin wasn't exactly well stocked. At any given time, I mostly had bread, peanut butter, Gummie Bears, and three or four hundred packets of ramen noodles lying around—none of which was an ingredient in of any of Angel's favorite recipes—especially the instant noodles. My "kitchen" consisted of a bathroom sink, the grill, the mini-fridge, a two-quart sauce pan and a handful of utensils—that's *counting* my beveled matte-cutter.

So Angel, who worked as a server's assistant at the Old Faithful Inn's restaurant, had to get whatever ingredients she could by flirting with the cooks and storekeepers there. We also made one trip to the ethnic isle of the nearest real supermarket which was 150 miles away in the nearest real town of Bozeman Montana. If we forgot to buy something *there*, we would definitely not be going back soon. We'd have to make due with what we already had.

And because you're probably wondering about this by now, I should point out that although the concessionaire that hires workers like Angel requires them to be of a certain age—18 if memory serves me correctly, and Angel (who told me she was 22), had to have provided them the proper documentation, there is the other rather ugly notion out there of what's known as an "American 22," versus a "Chinese 22"—if you know what I mean. If you don't know what I mean just watch the next women's Olympic gymnastics event. And Angel, in fact, looked the part of a 17-year-old gymnast (if not younger).

Furthermore, while I don't remember *when* exactly the *perception* of my life (by which all of maybe 50 people knew me), went from being Apprentice Dirtbag, to being Head Honcho of Creepy Incorporated International (PTE LTD), it was all just that—perception. My *actual* life consisted of innocently carving out a career, any way I could; innocently stroking my *ego*, anyway I could; and occasionally poking *fun* at those two pursuits . . . *anyway I could*—even if the latter meant reinforcing my perceived image as a *not*-so-innocent dirty old man.

And the purpose of the night in question (no matter what future inquisitors might say), was to simply have a nice home-cooked meal in my cabin. And it did, in fact, start out that way.

But we needed more pots and more pans. And I didn't really know my immediate neighbors well enough to borrow things from them. Besides, they might want to get in on the moo goo guy pan or whatever it was Angel planned to cook. So I frantically racked my brain, when it hit me. Jim and Donna! Of course. They lived in the trailer park on the other side of Old Faithful Village and were like regular normal people—not to mention my closest friends. They were among the (maybe 10), people who knew me as the earnest "dirtbag wannabe" that I really was, and could see through my "creepy guy" persona.

So I drove the Pedophiliamobile the two miles necessary to get to Jim and Donna's place, aware—but not particularly concerned—that the drive took me right past the ranger station. After all, I was legit now. But after acquiring said utensils, Donna asked me if I knew that my left brake light was out. So much for legitimacy I thought. And so I scribbled a note to get it fixed the next time I went to Bozeman.

Back at the cabin, it was decided we now needed curry, or some other such spice that we lacked.

Back to Jim and Donna's.

Then back to the cabin.

Then back to Jim and Donna's for something else.

Back to the cabin.

Then back to Jim and Donna's.

And anyone else, other than Jim and Donna would have started to get annoyed, but they had a sense of humor, a great sense of humor. You might even describe it as raunchy—which is one of the reasons I felt I could do what I did next—after Angel's final request.

This was actually a "two-parter" though. Yes, we needed cooking wine, but Angel, *being* an angel, thought it would be a nice gesture to give Jim and Donna, after all they'd done for us, our extra pork tenderloin—the one thing of which we bought too much.

And I agreed. But the problem was that Jim and Donna were in the middle of emptying, or trying to empty their gallon box of Mogen David Merlow into their own respective mouths when I again showed up at their door. And as it turns out, they didn't have any kind of container left in which to pour a portion of it, or at least any kind of container that wouldn't end up spilling all over my fine imitation-Corinthian leather seats. This, of course, is when I thought of Tommy—Tommy Tippy the sippy-cup that is.

So after emptying the sippy-cup of its coins, sanitizing it, and filling it with wine, I was once again on my way back to the cabin. But half-way there I noticed the tenderloin on the console. I'd forgotten to give it to them. Jim and Donna, as understanding as they are, upon one more knock at their trailer door, might have reached their breaking point when it came to neighborliness. But that's also when the dome light of my mind flickered on over my head. An Idea! A funny one at that!

The plan, although childish I have to admit, would be to position the pork tenderloin, which was vacuum-sealed in plastic, half-way out the fly of my pants before once again knocking on their door—sippy-cup in hand. They couldn't help but laugh out loud at that.

And as I sat parked in the Pedophiliamobile trying to just snug my zipper up next to the piece of meat in order keep it in place in my pants, but instead going a little too far with the zipper and getting it caught in the plastic (hopelessly caught, mind you), I noticed lights from a ranger's patrol cruiser.

And of all the things I *might* have said (while performing the sobriety test), answering Ranger Smythe's question regarding the sippy cup by stating that the wine in it was for a girl I had in my cabin and not for *me*, was the only thing I could manage. Well, I take that back. There was also some gibberish about moo goo guy pan that, in hindsight, after thinking about it for an entire off-season, might (to a ranger not concerned in the least by the Asian Invasion), just *might*, have sounded a little bit like baby talk.

And I'm guessing the trauma was so much for Ranger Smythe (that's ranger *Red* Smythe of the South Hampton Smythes), that he once again merely gave me a warning, this time to get my brake light fixed, and then muttered something about how he could have taken a job in his father's bank, before *then* driving off into the night, never to be seen or heard from again—at least by me.

I, however, drove off toward my cabin. To heck with Jim and Donna now.

And the trauma for me, if there was any, was in knowing there'd be no one around to later witness, even from a distance, Angel in her brave half-hour-long attempt to remove the stuck pork from my pants without damaging the zipper, not to mention my attempts to explain to her just how it got there (while, of course, also wondering what she might do if I tried to balance the sippy-cup on her head). Okay, there was also the matter of eating her moo goo guy pan or whatever it was she cooked. It was horrible, horrible food. Just because you *like* good food doesn't make you a good cook.

So as I sat in the Wheeled Womb—hail clouds on the horizon—and wondering how I would again wriggle into its sleeping "birth," for a fitful night of sleep, I tried to turn my thoughts to happy ones. Hail insurance. Yeah, that's it. And there may, indeed, come a time when I actually get some of that.

But there also may come a time when I get a newer, safer, more fuel-efficient vehicle—a used Volvo perhaps. A Volvo named Vulva. And I'll be sitting in it one off-season when that nostalgic feeling comes over me again. Who knows, I might even have the desire to return to the womb—the *Wheeled* Womb—as the Dent-Doctors of Psychology would put it.

Further Adventures in Booksitting:
The Satcom

"So, what are you selling here?"

Wow, I thought, you have to give him credit—he didn't confuse me with an information desk. But he *was* asking a question. And to a question like that I'll often respond by telling the person (who's usually surrounded by a spouse and/or kids), that I'm not *selling anything*, "I'm just autographing books."

"How much are they?"

"They're free," I'd reply. "The autographs, that is—heh heh."

The comeback would almost always come *back* in the form of a blank stare.

"The books are $24.95," I'd eventually respond.

"So what kind of writing do you do?" the patriarch of this particular family then asked.

"Basically, I steal every premise from every TV sitcom episode ever made, apply them to circumstances in *my* life, divide it all into 'chapters,' add a goofy title—and voila! I guess you'd call it short humor."

"But these look like they're just books of photography," the Ward Cleaver look-alike said after thumbing through a copy.

"They are. You asked me what I *wrote*."

"So where are your restrooms?" the man then asked. "June here just saw Old Faithful do its thing and it really made her have to pee."

And to this, I did what's commonly known (in TV circles anyway), as a "slow burn," all the while *thinking* about saying: They're not *my* restrooms. The Hotel at which I'm *not* employed, but doing a book signing for the benefit of my fans, *their* restrooms are down the hall-way and to the left.

But instead, I pointed out the fairly obvious restroom sign.

"Thanks pal," the man said, leaving a five on my table.

I pocketed the bill and sighed, "I bet Patrick McManus doesn't get tips at *his* book signings."

But who was I kidding. I was no Pattie Mac. I wasn't even Sherwood Schwartz. I only had three fans who weren't related to me (but who were, incidentally, related to each other)—all from Davenport Iowa. And I think *they* were just *pity* fans.

Then I saw Kyle.

Kyle wasn't necessarily a fan either, but he did have a way of mak-ing me feel better about myself.

"What's the matter Kyle? You look like someone just hurdled your 'closed for cleaning' sign, yanked you up by the collar, and slammed a stall door in your face again."

"Yeah," he said, "but that's not what's got me down."

"Then what is it? You look lower than the hem on June's skirt."

Kyle couldn't bring himself to speak.

"You can tell me," I said. "How long have we known each other? Weeks?"

"I've really gone and done it now," he confessed, before burying his head into his rubber-gloved hands. And as he slowly raised his head back out he added. "And now it's all happening—all happening so fast."

"What's all happening?"

Kyle squeegeed a tear from his cheek,

"My cousin who I haven't seen in years is coming to visit me next week—*here . . . in Yellowstone!*"

"And that's not a *good* thing?"

"You don't understand. We've just started e-mailing each other the last few weeks and . . ."

"And . . .?"

"And she somehow got the impression . . . that I was some kind of big-shot professional nature photographer."

"How did that happen?"

"I told her I was a big shot professional nature photographer."

"Boy," I then said with as much compassion I could muster, "are you ever going to be embarrassed when she gets here. It really looks like you got egg on your face. No wait, that's a kernel of corn. You might want to squeegee that off too."

A squeaking sound ensued.

"I got it," Kyle said, before mentally making a wish and blowing the kernel off his fingertip in my direction.

And while swerving out of the kernel's way I happened to notice June walking down the hallway all refreshed.

"It looks like you can go back to cleaning your toilets," I said before adding, "You know something Kyle? You sure do have a way of making me feel good about myself."

But for some reason I didn't really feel all that good. And as I saw Kyle walking away all dejected, I called out after him,

"Wait up Kyle, I have an idea."

Hey, I watched way too much TV throughout my life *not* to have an idea—*the* idea.

"What is it," he asked, a glimmer of hope now registering in his Sani-Flushed face?

"I'm scheduled to do a book signing at one of the general stores next week—one that I've never appeared at before."

"So?"

"So they've never *met* me. They don't know what I look like. And they definitely don't know you, you being a nobody and all. Are you starting to follow me?"

A sly grin formed on each of our faces. "Not a clue," he answered. "Is this one of those TV things, because I don't watch much TV. I find that it inhibits original thought, tends to make a person sedentary and . . ."

"This is where you shut up," I said, already referring to the plan.

I then went on to further explain "The Classic Switcheroo," whereupon *he*, in this case, would sign books for a day, and *I* would perform *his* porter duties. I would of course get paid (in advance), out of (Kyle's), pocket what Kyle normally earns for a day of portering. Kyle would get payment in the form of respect—from his cousin, his corny wish thus granted. And if any problems arose we'd be able to communicate via walkie talkie.

"But my cousin is due in the night *before* the book signing," Kyle said. "She'll see that I live in the employee dorms."

"No problem," I said. "You give me the key to your place and I'll give you the key to mine."

And so it went, without so much as even a hitch. And the proof of this lay in the walkie talkie transcripts (as provided by *your* NSA), below.

Kyle: When you said you had an RV, I was expecting something more than a *mini-van*. I was expecting something that you *pulled* with your mini-van. How do you *live* this way?

Me: Look Kyle, if this thing is going to go off without a *hitch*, you're going to have to put the plan into drive. Park creatively. And make up some sort of cover story, something so that your cousin won't even notice that you don't have a trailer hitch, or a trailer for that matter. I don't know why you had to tell her those things anyway.

Kyle: Maybe because I didn't want to seem like a *loser?*

Me: Look on the bright side, maybe she'll invite you to stay with her in *her* camper trailer.

Kyle: She already said she doesn't have enough room.

Me: Well it won't be any picnic for me either in this rickety old dorm. What is that—just a king-sized bed? And why is there a series of small holes in the ceiling? And do you really have to walk down the hallway to use the restroom?

Kyle: I think it's a Queen. And did you ever stop to think that you're on the first floor, where they house the guys, and that the second floor is where the girls live. And how far off in the *woods* do *you* have to walk to "use the restroom?"

Me: Oh yeah, that reminds me. If you should see a bottle of apple juice laying around, whatever you do, don't drink it.

After this there were some heavy redactions in the transcript text (a matter of national security, no doubt), but I remember that Kyle, after briefly meeting with his cousin, had found a relatively secure place to park and squeezed into the cramped "sleeping compartment/ office nook" of my "RV." And after scanning the ceiling with the pen light provided—an eerie scene, in and of itself, one that you might find in an X-Files episode (you didn't think I just watched situation comedies did you?)—we resumed uncensored communications.

Kyle: Where'd you get this mattress? Steal it from a wino on skid row? And why is there a series of small *paper scraps* on the ceiling of your van?

Me: They're notes, notes for the book I'm writing. That, and the push pins holding them in place also hold the ceiling fabric in place.

Kyle then read some of those notes out loud.

Kyle: "Use misunderstanding scene from 'My Mother the Car' pilot episode?"

Me: I'm calling *that* chapter: "My Car the Mutha'."

Kyle: "My Little Margarine Packet?"

Me: That one might be a tad too obscure. Oh, and if you happen to see my missing margarine packet, put it with the mayonnaise and cream cheese packets.

Kyle (still reading the notes): "Push pin, van ceiling, sleeping with mouth open scenario?"

Me: Look closer, that's *s'norio*. It's an original premise—a premise in progress actually, inspired, if you will, by a reoccurring nightmare. Hey, I don't steal *everything* from old sitcoms. And come to think of it, you might want to sleep on your side tonight.

Kyle: I can hardly move to turn over it's so cramped in here.

Me: I'm kind of riveted myself. Who *is* that living above you?

Kyle: Oh, that's Hazel—you know, the Goth chick from housekeeping. Yeah, I didn't recognize her at first either without her clothes, or from that angle. And tonight's a full moon. That's usually when her coven comes over to visit and they perform a bunch of weird rituals involving herbs that they rub on each other. I think she's part Sheepeater.

Me (weakly): Listen Kyle, you're starting to fade out. So to conserve on batteries I'm going to sign off for the night. But I'll be back in touch in the morning.

But before I could sign off completely, I heard him read one more note off the ceiling.

Kyle: "Say good night Gracie?"

Me: Good night Gracie.

The next morning, as I swept the hotel lobby's carpet, a near panicking Kyle got a hold of me.

Kyle: They've put me next to a $4.99 tee shirt sale display. It's crazy in here! No one's paying attention to me, and one lady even knocked me and my book signing table over to get to the shirts. What do I do?

Me: Tough it out. And be thankful you won't be mistaken for one of the tee-shirt racks itself. Besides they'll sell out by noon. At least that's what's happened at all the other general stores I've signed books at.

Kyle: Thank God. I don't know if I could stand the indignity much longer.

Me (changing the subject): Say, do you happen to know if the "up-stares [sic] maid" Hazel is working today? I have some interesting trivia for her.

And here's where the transcript got blacked out again. But I seem to remember a conversation with Kyle that closely resembled one held by a Mr. Bud Abbott and his good friend Lou Costello. Only instead of baseball, this conversation involved a 1960s TV show which, incidentally, had the same name as the aforementioned Goth housekeeper, and whose lead character, coincidentally, held the same (working), title. And there was, of course, a more than passing mention made of potion ingredients that each may or may not have used in her respective "cleansing" rituals, as the continued *un*redacted transcripts below show.

Kyle: Witch hazel?

Me: The one that looks more like Elizabeth Montgomery wearing black lipstick than the one on the TV show with the same name.

Kyle: Huh?

Me: Let me explain this again . . .

More redactions, followed by,

Kyle (getting back to the book signing): Oh no! Three bus-loads of Cub Scouts are unloading in front of the store. What's going to happen now?

Me: Well, first they'll come in, then the Scout leader will gather them all in front of your table and shout instructions for about a half-hour. Then they'll disperse and meet back at the same place in roughly an hour for more instructions.

Kyle: Oh, the humanity!

Me: In the meantime, a lot of the Scouts will linger by your table dripping ice cream on and bending the pages of your . . . er, my books. Some will ask you two or three questions about each and every photo in the books, which will keep people who actually have more than five dollars to spend from approaching your table. Oh, and I'm about to clean a toilet in the men's room—where do you keep the chlorine bleach?

Kyle: In the janitor's closet, on the shelf next to the material safety data sheets.

Me: Thanks. Good luck with those Scouts.

Kyle (a half-hour later): It's uncanny! All of what you told me has happened—just as you said. Except a woman did break through the crowd of Scouts to ask me for an autograph.

Me: Was she a somewhat more mature, single woman with a sequined visor?

Kyle: Yeah.

Me: Did she ask you to write something inspirational to her, and say she'd be back to pick up the book later, after she's through shopping?

Kyle: Yeah. What am I supposed to write? I'm no good at those kinds of things.

Me: Me either. That's why I keep a laminated list of stock phrases with me at all times. Try #12: "May you live all the days of your life."

Kyle: Thanks. Oh, and should I take her up on her offer?

Me: No! Believe me, she has more than friendship on her mind.

Kyle: That's what I thought.

Me: Is that the only signature you've given out so far today?

Kyle: No, now that you mention it. Earlier, before the Scouts arrived, a man asked me to sign a waiver. He said they were making a documentary. I didn't know if I should sign your name or mine, so I signed mine.

Me: That's weird. Those are usually signed after the fact. Was he from the Discovery Channel?

Kyle: I don't know. I'm thinking it might even be a foreign film. He told me some guy from another country—Borat I think his name was—might drop in later to interview me.

Me: Sounds pretty dull. Oh, by the way, I'm having some trouble with a really nasty stain in bowl 7. Where do you keep the ammonia, I'm going to try a chemistry experiment.

Kyle: It's in the janitor's closet next to the window cleaner—clear across the room from the bleach.

And that's where the transcript ends—with me soon after dropping my walkie talkie in toilet 7 just as the two highly reactive chemicals collided. It's also when I figured that radio communication was no longer necessary since they evacuated the whole hotel to made way for Wonderland Security officials. And it gave me the chance to mosey on over to the general store to see, in person, just how Kyle was doing. But, surprisingly, I only got as far as the general Store's parking lot, where I found Kyle staring into space.

"What's the matter? Did you get evacuated too," I asked him?

"Huh? Oh, no—it's just that it got a little too crazy in there for me. First some woman and her two kids came in and demanded I tell her what I did with you."

"Oh, that's right," I said. "My Three Fans were due in from Iowa this week. What'd you end up telling them?"

"I'm not really sure, it's all kind of a blur. Like I said, first the Iowa woman came in, then the foreign guy started molesting her—and vice versa. It's almost as if two highly reactive chemicals came into contact with each other. And I don't really think Cub Scouts should even see that sort of thing—let alone join in."

"Join in? How?"

"By hitting everyone involved with the books they bought."

"They all bought my book?"

"Yes, but that's not the point. The point is that it was *nuts* in there, especially when the old widow lady came back for her inscription and got caught up in the conga line."

"Wow!" I said with as much compassion as I could muster. "I bet your cousin wasn't very impressed. She did show up, didn't she?"

Kyle then got all quiet and confessed,

"There never was a cousin. The whole thing was a ploy to take the book proceeds under the table, and then make off with your RV, driving it to another country—hopefully one without an extradition agreement."

"Ah, the old '*Double* Switcheroo' first done on 'Sgt. Bilko' episode 11. But the books," I continued, "how'd you manage to sell so many?"

"I simply priced them at below 'extreme value tee shirt' prices."

"Ingenious!"

Kyle then handed me a roll of bills. "But I want you to have this," he said. "Put it toward some detailing on your 'RV's' interior. No one should have to live like you do."

Still puzzled (but all the while thinking that Dave Barry probably never got tips in the parking lot outside his *Barnes & Noble* appearances), I sputtered,

"But..."

"No buts," Kyle said. "Just give me back the key to my dorm room."

And that's when Wonderland-Security officials making their way across the same parking lot on their way from their second false alarm of the day had their first *legitimate* "situation"—breaking up what's been described as a level orange disturbance, a level orange disturbance over what's now commonly referred to as: The Sacred Key Incident (that, and the exclusive rights to a "maid"-for-*closed-circuit*-TV movie). Fortunately all of this resulted in only a few minor bumps and bruises—mild contusions—and nothing that a little witch hazel wouldn't eventually remedy.

Let Go and Let Dog

I'm done. I'm finished. I'm officially tapping out (as the kids say these days). And the phrase, "tapping out," is partly *why* I'm done. From what I can gather it comes from the world of Mixed Martial Arts and/or Ultimate Fighting. But I don't know. *Because I can't keep track of it all anymore!*

It began, though, with ambition—my high-strung sickly-child-hood ambition—and the road it took (or wouldn't take), through my Junior High School wrestling program.

The fact that during the competitions they would dock me points for every body slam was what totally threw *me*. That they even had a point system seemed a little strange. And my practice of waiting until the count of *two* before "kicking out" never ended well. How the hell was I going to become a pro-rassler with that kind of negative reinforcement.

It was enough to make a guy wondered if it wasn't all fake, if life wasn't all just an illusion.

So naturally, I started following boxing—the "sweet science" (as the old-timers call it). And much like real rassling, I got my knowledge of boxing from watching TV. I got to use it too—one day after Pop Warner football practice.

And who knows how it started. Who really knows how any kid-fight ever starts? You remember how they end though, and some of the middle, which had me jabbing, deftly, with my left, and following those lefts up with precise overhand rights. I was a combination of Mohammed Ali *and* Joe Frazier. And basically I had the kid reeling. I even remember at one point doing the Ali-Shuffle before sneaking in a Frazier-like short left hook that sent my opponent sideways into the chain-link baseball backstop. Down goes Wepner! The Marquis of Queensberry would have been proud.

I then started to feel a little sorry for the kid, who's name I don't remember but who I do remember lived literally on the other side of the railroad tracks, in the poor section of town, with his fifteen brothers and seventeen cousins, who, incidentally, were all considered thugs. So I waited politely for my opponent to get up, to perhaps finish him off, or, more likely, to call the whole fight off when the paradigm shifted.

That's because one particular member of the crowd that had gathered around to watch the fight, a crowd consisting of about fifteen brothers and seventeen cousins, that person got involved—creating a diversion. And when my head turned to *look* at the older brother jumping up and down waving the bag of football gear around his head, my opponent used this opportunity to send an under*handed* right *foot* to the medial-collateral ligaments holding together my un -cupped "groinicological" area. The next thing I knew my opponent was on my back—piggyback-style—(easy to do since I was already bent over), and both my nostrils were plugged by the fingers of his right hand. The fingers of his left were of course in my mouth tugging in the opposite direction, in an effort to fully open my face. In the end—bite marks interspersed with cleat marks all over my body— I lay sprawled out in the gravel, a victim of mixed-martial-arts

—if martial arts were mixed with industrial arts (that's how dirty they fought). The Marquis de *Sade* would have been proud.

And why mention this incident? Why write about the above? Who knows? Why bother *doing* anything? It's all been done! And done better, I might add. I'm sure in ancient Mayan times there was some form of wrestling, followed by some form of boxing, and then (when they became corrupted), there was some form of mixed-martial-arts—maybe even involving jaguars and sacrifices—ultimate fighting, or so they thought, at least until their civilization collapsed.

Furthermore, I'm sure that some "humorist" back then had already concocted the "comic" scenario of pro-rassling moves being performed in an amateur wresting venue. But as far as I know, it's original, and by the way, not concocted. I really did that stuff. I'm just that weird.

Even the point that it's all been done, has been done (hence the saying: there's nothing new under the sun). It's all just recycled and repackaged and re-hyped. A sprinter, for instance, can only run the hundred yard dash in so few seconds before reversing the earth's rotation and going back in time to where Mayan Jaguars are chasing him across the finish line—mixed *athletic* arts. A civilization reset button, therefore, really needs to be pushed, allowing us to start over. The Yellowstone supervolcano needs to erupt.

Because as it all began for me with ambition, my high-strung sickly-childhood ambitions, I can't help but remember my high-strung, sickly-young-adulthood ambitions—to be an artist, or when that became too difficult—a cartoonist. I wanted to be like Al Capp, or one of the illustrators in Mad magazine. But I was awful. And practice didn't seem to help. At one point I even put drawing salve on my fingertips every night, before waking up the next morning just as dreadful at drawing.

So I took up photography. Much easier—but much harder at which to make a living—at least in some ways. Because everyone wants to do it. They all think it's an easy career path. There's so much competition—and, therefore, so much pettiness.

But after twenty years or so of persevering, I landed the position of Resident Artist at one of the lodges in Yellowstone National Park.

Resident Artist—photography being one of he Mixed *Artistic* Arts (MAA)—consists of setting up shop (framed prints and a book signing table), in one corner of the lodge's lobby. In my case, that corner is right next to the entrance of the lodge's cafeteria, and of course, as always, right *above* the Yellowstone supervolcano caldera.

My duties are twofold and simple: to pimp my goods (as the kids are saying these days); and to get along with the visitors. These visitors, it seems, are twofold as well, either typical tourists, or professional photographer wannabes. But they're almost always on their way through the lobby to the cafeteria to fill some kind of void. I'm just an afterthought to them, or worse—a park information desk. And it's sometime hard to "keep a civil tongue" when answering general tourism questions. But sometimes they will actually recognize me as a photographer.

And as a longtime freelance nature photographer (who is currently Resident Artist), one of the questions I'm most frequently asked by visitors is: Do you enhance your photos?

This then normally leads to a spirited debate, and, of course, the inevitable follow-up question-of-semantics. But since I'm an equally longtime anti-semantic, and someone who is one snide remark away from (to borrow someone else's joke), becoming a *Sandwich* Artist in the nearby cafeteria, I'll usually just tell them a story, a story that reflects my ethic, and illustrates indirectly why I think that "enhancement" question is inherently insulting.

You see, I've always prided myself as doing things the honorable way, from using the Marquis of Queensberry rules—in a kid street fight, to the practice of (unless otherwise noted), using all original material in my stories, or at least as original as anything can be under this particular sun.

And in my attempt to broaden my photographic horizons I traveled to among other places—Thailand. And during my second full winter of scouting that beautiful country I got an idea for a shot. It was of a beautiful open-aired Buddhist shrine at the top of a mountain. As usual, I envisioned early morning light, and patchy fog for the conditions. So after I finally managed to communicate the time and place to my Thai taxi driver, he showed up at my hotel an hour late. And the conditions that morning were, indeed, ideal—the only problem, of course, being that I was approximately one full hour away from the summit and my intended subject *during* those ideal conditions.

When I tried it again a few weeks later, my driver showed up on time, but the conditions were average at best.

And I should point out here that climbing the steps to this mountaintop shrine isn't easy. There are about 1,400 of them. And a lot of the steps, in a lot of the stretches, can be used as hand-holds. They're that steep. Throw in eighty-degree temps, seventy-percent humidity, and two packs of photo equipment, and you might even to call it *work*—depending on your fitness level.

So with dwindling ambition, but ambition nonetheless, this still rather high-strung, sickly adult—with the aerobic capacity of a sea anemone (an anemic anemone even)—this sickly adult tried it once again. And this time I made it to the top in time. The conditions were looking good too. I soon realized, though—while composing the shot—that I needed my other camera, and when I turned for my pack to get it, I saw that the pack wasn't where I put it, but was instead being swung over the head of a hopping macaque monkey, a macaque monkey with a menacing smirk on his face.

I then realized that I'd been surrounded by a gang of monkey thugs, and was in the process of being mugged. And as I began wrestling with the one monkey for the small pack, another monkey jumped on my other pack—a backpack still on my back. It's almost as if the one monkey had used a diversionary tactic in order to enable the other monkey (one of his fifteen brothers or perhaps one of his seventeen cousins)—to get the drop on me.

And after I spun the one monkey off my back, and finally regained the camera bag from the other, I saw that the photographic moment had passed. The sun went behind a cloud, never to be seen again the rest of the morning.

I tried it again a few days later, and let's just say that some bad mayonnaise and a "shart" half-way up the mountain was involved in my not getting the shot that time, not to mention my being fully blackballed from the Ao Nang Town & Country Taxi Coalition.

The very next *winter*, I learned how to rent a motorbike and how to drive to the base of the mountain temple by myself. Average conditions again led to no shot. The road conditions on the way back to my hotel, however (a large pothole that had appeared out of nowhere), led to a week of my rehabbing from severe road-rash and some sprained joints.

And so after that setback, I again arrived at the base of the mountain at 5:00 am. This time two stray dogs had found me and kept me company all the way up—barking loudly and nipping at my heels. But the atmospheric conditions were perfect. Wispy fog floated through the jungle covered hills and the eastern sky was crystal clear and slowly turning a beautiful shade of pink. The dogs had left, and the sun would soon be illuminating the three life-sized Buddhist statues— seated, meditating Buddhist statues—that would be my foreground. And that, of course, is when the two stray dogs came back and began cavorting around in the foreground, all but ruining the scene.

That's also when I first decided to tap out. I was finished. Done. What was the point of *doing* anything? So I took a deep breath and just sat there quietly. And then I took another deep breath—and then another. And before I knew it, I think I was—*meditating*—like the statues in front of me.

Something then compelled me to pick up my camera as one of the stray dogs left, and the other began sniffing the rear-end of one of the statues. I smiled at this—still relaxed—still breathing. I then waited a few seconds for something else to happen—camera at the ready. And that's when the dog circled to the front of the scene and posed perfectly—making eye contact with one of the statues. It's like he was receiving (or imparting), some sort of wisdom.

That's also when the index finger of my right hand reflexively twitched downward on my camera's shutter, capturing the moment, *and* what would be my favorite picture of all time—the God-Dog shot.

Fast-forward to the next summer in the Old Faithful Lodge's lobby, as I sat in the midst of a crowd of Yellowstone tourists, crying babies to the left of me, would-be professional photographers to the right, where someone asked me a question, a question, believe it or not, about—photography,

"What's your favorite photograph that you've taken?" the guy asked.

I thought for awhile, then rummaged through a bin, and then finally handed him the God-Dog print,

"Wow, that *is* nice . . ." he said. And then, after scrutinizing the print some more he continued, ". . . did you Photoshop that dog into the picture?"

The supervolcano inside of me began to seethe and then to rumble. But then I took back the print and reexamined it. I took a long deep breath, or two—or three—and relived the scene. It's when I tapped out again,

"Yes," I told him. "The photo's fake . . . like pro rassling. In fact, everything you see here is an illusion."

The tourist then left—smug and self-satisfied, a superficial void filled.

But I knew the truth—me and my Dog-Spelled-Backwards.

Epilogue

By now you're probably convinced that not only am I the worst photographer to make his or her entire living from the sale of his work, but that I'm now the worst *writer* to make fourteen dollars and ninety-five cents from the sale of his *writing*.

My guess is you judged the book by its cover (which was good enough to fool *you*), before going home and reading the introduction. Then, for some unexplained reason, you skipped ahead to this page and are now wondering just how you can get your $14.95 back.

And I'm hoping you're not the only one.

Because "Jumbo" (go back and reread the introduction), has just had to have one of his tusks surgically removed and "our" insurance policy has a deductible equal to or greater than the US welfare and military budgets combined. I'm writing this epilogue while sitting on a beach chair *in Nebraska* (while "we" recover), and due to my insecurity as a photographer, just bought the latest and most expensive Hoyt-Clagwell DSLR they have. If the images I get from it aren't

good enough to convince anyone to publish my next book *of pho-*
tography, I'm at least thinking that there might be one good enough
for the cover of my next book of *prose*—even more assorted sordid
stories from which you can have buyers' remorse. And guess what.
You're not getting your money back on that one either.

"My conjoined twin was a Siamese monkey—and an only child!"
David Peterson

David Peterson grew up looking at photo books, books
like *Mountain Light*, by Galen Rowell, and *Our
National Parks*, by Ansel Adams. He then learned how to read,
and got his hands on such scholarly works as: *My Brother Was
an Only Child*; *Never Sniff a Gift Fish*; and *Man's Search for
Meaning*.

So it stood to reason that Dave would eventually try his hand
at becoming a professional landscape photographer, and then
(after underachieving in that regard), *writing* about his fail-
ures—photographic misadventures in such far-off places as
Borneo, New Zealand, and Thailand (formally the Kingdom
of Siam)—where, incidentally, the above awkward monkey
moment happened.